T4-AIG-012

GROWING A RAINBOW

The Premature Journey of a Two Pound Hero

Aquhorthies

Publishing

This publication is sold with the understanding that the author and Aquhorthies Publishing are not engaged in rendering medical, legal or other professional advice or services.

Though this book is a recollection of events, some of the names and distinguishing traits of persons within the publication have been changed (the number of Irish doctors was not).

Copyright © 2014 Lesley Donaldson-Reid writerlesleydonaldson.com

Blog posts taken from realwomendrivestick.com

Published in Canada by Aquhorthies Publishing 3-1750 The Queensway, Suite 1312, Toronto ON M9C 5H5

Thank you for buying an authorized edition of this book and for complying with copyright laws by not reproducing, scanning or distributing any part of it in any form whatsoever without permission from the author. All rights reserved.

For permission requests contact aquhorthies@bell.net

Library and Archives Canada Cataloguing in Publication

Donaldson-Reid, Lesley, 1973-, author
Growing a rainbow : the premature journey of a two pound hero / Lesley Donaldson-Reid.

Issued in print and electronic formats.
ISBN 978-0-9937823-0-5 (pbk.).--ISBN 978-0-9937823-1-2 (pdf)

1. Premature infants. 2. Premature infants--Care. 3. Parent and infant.
I. Title.

RJ250.3.K78 2104   618.92'011   C2014-905092-5
                                              C2014-905093-3

Your purchase supports premature infants through the Canadian Premature Babies Foundation (cpb-fbpc.org)

Cover Design & wall mural art:
2014 © Desiree Kern, Greyscale Studios greyscalestudios.com

Cover photograph: 2014 © Lesley Donaldson-Reid

All other photographs: 2014 © Diana Nazareth Photography www.diananazareth.com

Formatting for digital and print publishing provided by:
Doris Chung, Publisher Production Solutions publisher-ps.com

Printed in China

To Torran, the soul outside my body.
To Bruce, my anam cara.

My boys:
Thank you both for letting me share you with
the world.

ACKNOWLEDGEMENTS

I extend the following personal thanks regarding the self-publishing of my manuscript:

To the families and babies I've mentioned: Thank you for trusting me with the treasure that is your extraordinary life stories.

To Karen Marciano: You are an inspirational measure of my writing success.

To Jennifer Powell: This niche blogger evolved into a self-published author because of the Blissdom Canada Conference (thanks to your team!). Also, thank you for helping me find my brand(s).

To Michelle Walker: For taking time away from your family to share your editing skills with my passion, thank you.

To my early readers, most notably Katharina Staub, Mark Ellis, and Cynthia Hill: Thank you for giving me your enthusiasm, expert guidance and encouragement.

To Doris Chung: For your mentorship and your tireless assistance with revisions, I am deeply grateful.

To the Canadian Premature Babies Foundation: Your support of my work means a great deal. I'm pleased that I'm able to contribute to the valuable work of your organization.

AUTHOR'S NOTE

I could fill a book with our gratitude.

We survived the NICU, in part, because our families by birth and by choice showed us as much love as we gave Torran. We are ever thankful for their support.

Bringing home a baby like Torran takes teams of people, some of whom you won't meet in this story. From cleaners to clinicians, these people are very special to my family. We cannot thank them enough for running the facilities Torran needed to survive and for giving him a chance to live.

On Torran's journey, you'll find staff you like and some you don't. Such is the nature of human beings. Even though we had some unpleasant experiences, we honour all the people who worked with our son.

Where I quoted professional staff, I did so to the best of my recollection during the time when I kept an online journal about Torran's hospitalization. Any errors are my own.

Prematurity isn't simply a matter of an early birth. Sometimes it's a dramatic struggle for life. It sets the tone for a different kind of parenting, especially in the family's first years.

In this re-telling of our life, you may not see the full treasury of hugs sent to our family, both physical and spiritual. Those family, friends, colleagues and strangers gave us the crutches we needed to carry on each day.

I wanted to tell our story, and by extension, that of thousands of parents across Canada. You'll meet some of the families we shared time with in the NICU, and their wonderful babies. If you're still in the hospital, or know someone struggling in the NICU, know that there comes a day when things won't be so hard. For all families, I wish that your babies come home healthy and happy. I hope this book is gives your heart armor.

Prematurity is a global phenomenon. The number of babies born premature is increasing, as is the use of technology to give them life. I strongly encourage you to learn about prematurity and its effects on families by contacting your local prematurity awareness group, or the Canadian Premature Babies Foundation.

RED

DECEMBER 6, 2007 TO MARCH 7, 2008

CHAPTER I

MARCH 10, 2008, 3:00 A.M.

There are no more cries in the labour and delivery rooms; babies and mothers rest in silence. I was the last of three high risk mothers giving birth tonight. My baby, The Peanut, was taken away before I could touch him. Bruce and I sit in the darkened room, wondering what is happening to our child.

I'm glad the epidural is so strong. After 40 minutes in the operating room, three doctors, two anaesthesiologists and two nurses finally managed to remove the last of The Peanut's mangled placenta. I didn't feel any of the trauma.

Bruce rests his head on the stretcher beside mine but he can't sleep either. He hasn't kissed me so much since the day he found out about my pregnancy. It amazes me that he's been up for almost 24 hours.

Dr. Sharifi, the senior neonatologist on-call arrives to update us. He stands in the doorway, a million miles away. I was pregnant for 26 weeks and six days instead of 40 to 42 weeks. I won't have a third trimester. This man knows whether my child is alive.

He begins by reviewing the risks associated with the premature birth of our 26 week old baby. The delay gets on my nerves.

"I'm a nurse, I understand." *Did he stand a hint straighter with that abrupt interruption? So much for being the cooperative patient.* The salt tracks on my face dissolve in newly escaped tears. "Is my baby breathing?"

His answers reach me like lava.

"Initially, he breathed on his own for four minutes." *Four minutes! How glorious! But, get to the point.*

"Then we needed to help him by putting a tube into his lungs to give him a mix of oxygen and nitrogen. He responded well at first. But, he's only incorporating 60% of the oxygen into his bloodstream. We'll give him some other medications to help that number increase, but I can't predict what will happen."

My bubble burst. *That's not a healthy oxygen level.*

A young woman in scrubs steps into the room, offering me tissues. "Would you like to see him?"

I'm deafened by the words. The Peanut is the only baby left in the resuscitation room, and the staff are making an exception to accommodate me in a stretcher. The epidural puts me a risk for falling if I walk because I can't feel my legs. They roll me to the resuscitation room, a floating Roman on my medical divan.

The small room is full of technical junk. To one side is an open air incubator. Lisa, the respiratory therapist who stole my baby earlier now greets me with a welcoming gesture as she fiddles with controls on the ventilator.

Centred in the incubator, there is a pale, naked little body. Lines stick out of his navel connected to an intravenous pump. His nostril has a huge straw sticking out of it; a smaller tube winds out of his mouth. The neonatal intensive care nurse who brought us to the room is named Heather. She explains that our baby swallowed and inhaled a lot of blood during delivery and they're trying to remove it.

The Peanut's arms reach out randomly with wrinkled fingers but he cannot fully extend his elbows. Two legs kick towards a phantom uterus, waving around the red oxygen sensor taped to one foot. He is not content with his new surroundings.

His face is incredibly round and his eyelids swollen. Dried blood clings to his bloated skin.

My Peanut doesn't look like I expected.

I'm afraid that my voice would be too loud in the open air. Leaning forward, I put my finger into his warm hand.

"Hello there. I'm your mummy." *Will I ever stop crying?* Five angelically manicured nails curl around my fingertip.

"Okay, that's weird," Lisa says, "his oxygen just jumped up, like, 20%. He must know his mommy is here."

Humbled by this miniature version of himself, Bruce has another little happy cry. My tears haven't stopped.

"Does he have a name?" Heather prepares to write it on the sheet underneath him. *She writes, therefore he is.*

Torran.

DECEMBER 06, 2007

Ambivalent snow descends from the dark sky beyond the window. It covers the single animal track leading from the tree on my lawn to the house. By tomorrow, the animal's existence will be buried. I fog my breath on the pane and draw a stick figure face. Condensation trickles down across its cheek and slides into the down curved mouth.

The orange tinge of the street lamp inserts itself past me into the room. No other lights glow indoors except for the one in *that room* down hall. I brave the corridor towards the bathroom. Harsh white bands seep from the edges of the door. To the left, my bedroom door remains closed. Floorboards cry out with each slow step. I don't remember the hallway being this long.

It's not the half-avocado sized clot of blood partially submerged in the bowl which makes me nauseous. It's the thought of what I might find when I reach in to break it apart: my unborn child.

The bleeding started seven weeks ago. I'm used to it now, and I know it's not altogether an uncommon phenomenon for pregnant women.

Earlier today I thought the bleeding was over. The thirteenth week of my pregnancy passed without blood after a period of three days. I felt immense relief when we returned tonight from a trip in the United Kingdom to visit our families.

But I was wrong. The bleeding hadn't stopped. Maybe there is something to the unwritten Commandment of Pregnancy: *Thou shalt not tell people of your pregnancy until the second trimester in case you have a miscarriage.* The common belief is a woman is supposedly "out of the woods" after twelve weeks of pregnancy and can share the news without worry.

My hand starts the maternal rub starts on its own. My belly is still more fat than baby at present. Before any problems started, I announced my news at work when I was four weeks pregnant.

When my nursing co-workers critically scanned my belly I'd grab the generous curve of my lower abdomen and joke, "This is baby food!" The nickname "The Peanut" stuck at six weeks, after the baby's fetal size.

Corinne, one of the charge nurses, and mother of three, cautioned me against sharing the news so early. "Aren't you afraid to jinx yourself? What if something happens?"

"Honey, if I'm going down, you're all coming with me!" I responded. *That was when I used to be playful about being pregnant.*

I don't know what to do about this blood clot. My husband, Bruce, is asleep, trying to overcome jet lag before work.

Grumbling about my night-owl tendencies, but willing to support me, he'd get up and join me in the bathroom. As I investigate the clot, he'd cringe and probably avert his eyes. He'd sit with me while I cry, regardless of the outcome. Sleep will cure my sorrow, he'll tell me.

I reconsider waking him up. His presence won't change whether or not there is a baby in the red lump. If he should put two planes too close together in the sky because I interrupted his sleep, I'd never be able to forgive myself. I don't need more guilt.

I dry heave as I think about a blue fetus with a thumb in its mouth. Our child is the size of half a banana with arms, legs and a face. Sitting on the cold tiled floor, I hold my breath and reach into the bloody water.

I squeeze my eyes and hand shut. The congealed tissue is the consistency of thick Jell-O, without a bony mass. Exhaling, I open my eyes. Several plum sized blood boats drift in a calm red sea. My arm juts out like a Nova Scotia lighthouse.

The too-familiar ferric smell worsens my nausea and makes me throw up. Sobbing, I bring myself to my feet and flush the entire unsightly mess down the drain. Like Lady Macbeth, I scrub the blood from my hand vigorously, my ferocity stemming from a fear of bacteria rather than guilt.

I look down at my abdomen, all fat and baby. "Thank you Peanut. Thank you for staying in Mummy." I chastise myself for thinking Corinne was right.

The queasiness eases. I sit down at my computer next to the empty nursery. There's time to deal with that.

My hands fidget on the keyboard aimlessly. Do I research about pregnancy and bleeding on the internet again? Or do I find something more distracting and less stressful to do for a couple of hours before I can't sit here anymore? The traffic signal at the nearby intersection glows red through the small window.

This latest gynecological episode means I can't return to work in the emergency department. Nothing is going the way I planned.

When the bleeding started, Dr. Tasker, my fertility doctor, suggested that I had an implantation bleed. She suspected that the embryo lodged itself near a particularly vascular part of my uterus.

"Spotting is an acceptable part of a first trimester," she said in response to the pink-brown discharge in my sixth week.

7

In my ninth week, I passed a plum-sized clot during heavy bleeding on an overtime night shift. She met with me the next morning. Her dark hair, which always looked wind-blown, was pulled back into a neat ponytail.

"You may have a marginal abruption, at the edge of the placenta. The placenta can't adhere to the uterus lining when there is active bleeding. The lifted section sometimes collects blood underneath it, which is called a subchorionic bleed. The placenta has a lot of redundancy built into it. If one area is bleeding, the rest can compensate and Baby will be just fine. It should level itself out by the thirteenth week, when the hormones plateau and the placenta matures."

The Peanut grew in a room where the wallpaper can't stick to a wet wall. That's a bit of an interior design flaw.

The hemorrhaging was painless, a good sign because women who miscarry often feel strong cramping sensations. Still, Dr. Tasker removed me from work for safety. Stress has adverse effects on pregnancy. Nurses in emergency departments do not have laid back jobs. I welcomed the house arrest and took the financial hit. At least I didn't require complete bed rest.

I type PLACENTAL BLEEDING into the computer ignoring the advice I've given to patients about relying upon Dr. Google. As I expect, there is a lot of copy-paste information about the many reasons women bleed in the first trimester. I read countless statements from anxious mothers-to-be. *Why don't we talk about it?*

I see the headline "Getting Pregnant After 35" and roll my eyes into my head. Bruce and I are late bloomers. We married in our early 30s, after three long years of overseas courtship. We didn't live in the same country until one month after our wedding. Being the child of a prolonged divorce, I wanted to test our married life before we involved children. It meant pushing a pregnancy very close to that foreboding age of 35.

A year later, we threw out the birth control, ready to start a family with three kids. Six months passed without success and I insisted on consulting a fertility clinic to move things along faster. My ovaries made suitable sized eggs but had difficulty releasing them.

We became our own lab rats. Our lovemaking needed to be scheduled and purposeful. I pushed sex to meet a calendar deadline. Sometimes that induced performance anxiety in Bruce. At other times, I refused him, for fear of dislodging an embryo.

It always seemed like we had visitations to or from overseas family when I ovulated. As I click through the web, sifting through boundless self-help sites without finding new information, I smirk at the time I told Bruce, "I don't care if your 70 year old Auntie is across the hall. I worked last night and will do so tonight. This morning is the only time I have to make this baby." I'm sure she heard us, thinking that we were horrid hosts for exposing her to the sounds of our baby-making.

My menses was late just as this year's Father's Day approached. I mentally planned a dinner for two, with one glass of wine, one of milk, and a Father's Day card from an unborn child. In the end, the only gift I gave Bruce was a crying wife and her unwanted menstruation.

After each unsuccessful month with the clinic, using pills, injections and monitoring procedures to no avail, I increasingly contemplated stepping up the assisted reproductive technologies ladder. Two years after we married, we considered intrauterine insemination, an option that further depletes emotions and money.

"Lesley, I'm not going to stand in an office and watch them inject you with my sperm," Bruce argued about the IUI. For the first time, I felt he faltered as my supportive partner. "It's bad enough that I have to wank off into a container at 6:00

a.m. I can't be arsed seeing you with your feet in the air and a big turkey baster in your fanny."

"So you don't want to be in the room when your child is conceived, Bruce?" I hoped my words hit home.

"Look, you know me. I don't like medical stuff. I'll go with you if I have to but, no, I don't want to watch. There's nothing I can do in there."

Our conversation ran around in circles like this for days, neither of us accepting the other's position. As it turned out, I wasted my haughtiness. We conceived through timed sex and induced ovulation in our last pseudo-normal attempt before the unromantic IUI in the clinic.

And then the bleeding started, replacing jokes about second trimester orgasms with angst and physical separation. My world still revolved around my uterus but the life I previously obsessed about vanished.

I begin my blog post, telling someone - anyone, about my bleeding, fearing the start of my second trimester.

CHAPTER 2

JANUARY 11, 2008

I pass through the renovated lobby in Trillium Health Centre, West Toronto, expecting the myriad faces in the wall mural to greet me in unison like the staff of The Mandarin restaurant. The larger composite mouths remain open, transmitting their welcome message telepathically. The two story reception soothes visitors with its oxygenating walls of plants and a stylized waterfall. It makes me want to pee. It was the wrong entrance to choose when I'm holding four cups of water in my bladder.

The older ultrasound department lacks the sexiness of the lobby. I'm lying on stretcher behind a curtain. Sunlight isn't allowed in here. Machines dictate the design of the space.

But it doesn't bother me. I'll go anywhere to treat my "Peek-a-Boo I see you" withdrawal symptoms. During my first trimester, the fertility clinic monitored me twice a week with blood tests and ultrasounds.

Nurses poked me to measure my progesterone and beta-HcG levels. I inserted a waxy progesterone suppository into my rectum four times a day, maintaining the hormonal glue. The icky mess and constipation it caused made me very uncomfortable.

I can't say that I want to return to those first trimester days, but I do miss the weekly ultrasounds. Being a medically-managed expectant mother gave me the privilege of watching The Peanut grow. Each week held a different stage of wonder: from the pulsating glow that was the first heart beat, to the alien phase when The Peanut's eyes looked almost as big as its head, I marveled at the miracle that is my developing baby.

Bruce's shift pattern prevented him from attending most of these appointments. He saw The Peanut when it looked like a lawn grub. However, he's bonding through the pictures I bring home and the kisses his gives to my belly.

Today I'll get another image of our child. I hesitate to tell people how fantastic I feel, like I'm somehow betraying another Commandment of Pregnancy. It's almost a good thing I have little contact with the outside world during my "sick leave." No one can rat me out to the Pregnancy Police.

I have few symptoms of pregnancy, apart from the bleeding. 30 seconds of nausea washed over me, once. In the afternoon I nap even though my days are exceptionally boring. In fact, were it not for the twice a week blood tests, rectal medications and ultrasounds, I would doubt that I'm pregnant. Except that I think I felt The Peanut move. *How exciting!*

The twinge came last week and I didn't think much of it. Unusual discomforts in the abdomen often result from the uterine muscles and tendons stretching as they accommodate a growing baby. The sensation intensified over the last little while.

During the eighteen week structural ultrasound two weeks ago, The Peanut refused to reveal its heart. I'm back to try again. And I hope for visual confirmation that my latest sensation is fetal movement.

If you hide your heart again Peanut, we can see each other next week.

The technologist, Anne, squeezes the ultrasound gel bottle, making a wet farting sound. To prevent myself from giggling, I tell her about my plans for a baby shower. It'll be nice to have an excuse to have people over.

She reaches across me for a tricky picture. Her arm smells of hospital sanitizer. I crane my neck upwards trying to see my child moving in grainy shades of black and white. She frowns as she wipes off her equipment.

"You know that you don't have any amniotic fluid?" she says, more statement than question.

One summer I rode the drop tower at Canada's Wonderland. My heart thundered as the carrier rose 200 feet into the sky. The car released and I plunged down at 100 kilometers per hour. My lungs disconnected from my chest and I stopped breathing. Brief and thrilling at the time, that feeling hits me now, carrying doom in its wake. I'm frozen in an unbelievable moment. I manage to squeak out words.

"I have a subchorionic bleed, and one time they found an abruption," I defend my uterus, "but that's all." Speaking prompts me to breathe.

"I have to get the radiologist to check the images. Sorry, I thought you knew. You know, it might not be all that bad." She speaks quickly as she backs out of the room.

The detergent smell remains behind and suffocates me. The ultrasound gel on my belly decreases a million degrees. I get goose bumps, but it's not from the cold goop.

Something is terribly, terribly wrong.

He has to have fluid! I saw him moving! I felt it!

Then I remember Saturday morning's bleeding was different, brown and slightly watery on the pad. *Is that when it happened?* There wasn't a huge gush of fluid as one would expect with the rupture of amniotic membranes. Then again, I'm not nine months pregnant.

I wipe myself clean and put my hand on my lower abdomen feeling The Peanut move. Mother and son reassure each other until the technologist returns.

An hour later, I bury myself beneath a blanket on my couch. I can't stop sobbing. My appointment with an obstetrician isn't for another eight weeks. Without a doctor following my care, the hospital's on-call OB must see me to discuss my options.

Options? What options?

I resist the overwhelming desire to pace around the living room. Lying down prevents gravity from sucking out what little fluid I have left in my uterus. Or so I tell myself.

A hand (*it must be mine, right?*) picks up the phone and dials a number, putting it to my ear. My sister answers. My wall of strength collapses. A voice I don't recognize blurts out the critical finding into the receiver.

"I need you to come over now. Can you come? Please?" I succumb to the anxiety in my chest. I cannot wait alone.

Bruce isn't due home for 45 minutes. I won't interrupt him with this news. Hundreds of people in the sky need him right now. My dire situation isn't going to change if he leaves work early.

Jessica arrives at the door, eyes reddened. Our hug lasts longer than any I can remember, tears falling on each other's shoulders. I can't speak. She waits.

Our mother told us one was the milkman's; the other the mailman's. Jessica's brown eyes and light brown hair contrast to my blue eyes and dark blonde hair. She's younger but was often mistaken for being older. Jes married first and had a son seven years ago. In our youth, I envied her slim build to my heavier body size. We've never looked more alike than now when we both battle our weight.

Nearly opposites of each other, we had an uneasy sisterhood, save for moments when life took a huge swing at one of our heads.

I know Jessica wants details about the possible outcomes. She holds back her inquisition. I dump my worries on her instead of Bruce. He can't handle this intense emotion very well, probably because he can't fix it.

It isn't long before a gust of Toronto's bitter winter wind blows Bruce through the door. His smile falls quicker than I did on the drop tower when he sees his devastated wife and her sister, a pile of tissues between them.

I barely give him time to digest the situation, telling him we have to return to the hospital. My sister escorts us to the door. Her lips purse together as she wishes us good luck. My eyes tear up again but I deny the overwhelming wave of sorrow. She gets the strongest hug I can muster, from a big sister who feels very small.

We head straight to the labour and delivery unit. Dr. Blake speaks to us candidly about the ultrasound result.

"You fluid index is 3.1 centimetres. It should be five. We call this situation oligohydramnios." Bruce and I remain mute. She can't confirm that my amniotic membranes ruptured. Dr. Blake didn't see anything on either my internal physical exam or the slide of fluid she sampled.

"50% of women with a spontaneous rupture of amniotic membranes deliver within one week. Of those women, 50% deliver within twenty four hours. You're past that first week, but there's no way of predicting what comes next."

The loss may be from a hole in the sac or a problem with the production of fluid by the baby. When a fetus pees, it creates amniotic fluid. If the fetus's kidneys aren't working, amniotic levels will be low. Fetal swallowing may also be the cause. I don't have the other risk factors associated with the disorder: diabetes, placental insufficiency, hypertension or dehydration.

Oligohydramnios leads to serious problems, even if the fetus survives to the age of viability. The Peanut won't have room to grow, conveying another host of problems including skeletal and organ deformity.

She leaves the most pressing danger to the end. "A baby uses amniotic fluid to practice breathing. If there is no fluid, Baby's lungs cannot develop and may become hypoplastic, meaning they can't inflate properly." Dr. Blake keeps her tone sympathetic.

"There's nothing I can do to improve what's happening. I might have to induce an early delivery for your safety if you get an infection. I'll put you on antibiotics to help prevent that. At this point, you have two options. You can wait to see what happens, although the chances for you to remain pregnant remain slim. Or, you can terminate your pregnancy."

This is not a suggestion for which we are prepared. We drive home in silence, Bruce staring straight ahead. I turn away from him, wasting precious fluid on my face. We head home, not knowing if The Peanut will survive the night.

JANUARY 31, 2008

Pings and knocks in the heating vents have a debate over who is going to make more noise, them or me. My fingers tap on lettered squares as I balance a keyboard on my raised knees. It wakes Bruce at seven o'clock.

"Lesley, what are you doing up so early?" He wipes the grunge out of his eyes and stands to his full six foot two height. His softly defined muscles carry his rumpled boxer shorts like an oversized blonde child.

"I thought I'd get a head start on shoveling." I know he'll appreciate my sarcasm. Bruce glances at the lengthy email on the computer screen alongside the bed. Sitting at a desk isn't an option, so we've brought the computer into the bedroom on a low rolling shelving unit.

"You didn't do that before you got up the duff." He looks onto the accumulation of snow in the garden. Snowflakes drift down, afraid to come to rest, lest they lose their individuality in the two feet that preceded them. "Right. I'm going to do the drive. Good thing I like the cold. How's the leaking?"

I shrug. "Same, I guess. There's been no real bleeding since that bout yesterday." My Uterus Report is a daily phenomenon.

"I'm worried about you not getting any exercise or anything." He pulls on a short sleeved shirt and cargo pants, his typical winter wear.

"What do you expect me to do? When I get up I can feel it coming out. I didn't lift a single suitcase whilst we were in the UK and that's when I still had fluid. Why would I start exerting myself now?" The hand he can't see grips the blanket beside me as I stare him down.

"I know. But…" he falters. The zipper on his trousers suddenly becomes troublesome, demanding his attention. I know Bruce's conscience struggles between his athletic instinct and the logic of complete bed rest. "You're still allowed to walk around. The doctor said bed rest won't make things better."

"Look," I feel a familiar anger spreading up my neck, "the doctors may not care whether or not I have this baby, but I do. If all I can do is lie here and drink four litres of fluid a day, hoping that a small portion of it will go into my uterus and stay there, then that's what I'm going to do!" My short fuse peaks, daring him to engage.

He pulls his shirt tighter over his chest, opens his mouth and then closes it. Bruce kneels on the bed leaning over to me precariously.

"Well, just stretch your legs in bed or something." He kisses my forehead and leaves the room, his medicine prescribed. The driveway he can fix.

I return to the email I'm writing to the two women I recently met online. Most of my friends haven't experienced these kinds of problems. Though sympathetic to me, I feel like I can't show them that I'm petrified. So, I reached out to women who have never met me before.

Naomi is an American matched with me through a pregnancy support website. She had similar placental problems. Shelly's blog was the sliver of hope I'd found for continuing my pregnancy. Her daughter wasn't severely disabled or dead like all the other information I'd found on the effects of babies born from oligohydramnios. Both women hold my hands electronically day after day through my crying, boredom and those horrible fears of losing The Peanut.

I write: *Yesterday was the kind of day where I said to myself, "do I have to leak so much?" I never thought in my life that a tablespoon of fluid could hold so much power over me. Yes, I measured.*

I woke up at 4:30 in the morning as I've done frequently during my first trimester. Bruce was getting ready for work. After seeing the overnight's output (noticeably more than the previous couple of nights) I lay in bed having my daily commune with Fate, the gods, and basically any other ethereal being who would listen.

Of course, I had myself a little cry too. But I didn't want Bruce to know. I already woke him up with a nightmare on Tuesday; I dreamt I was on a stretcher in an operating room screaming for someone to save my baby. The baby was coming out and I couldn't help it. There was no one around.

Previously, I wrote to them about my anger over my failure as a woman. I want to tell them about the rawness of the skin in my groin from wearing feminine pads for the last three months. Most of all, I want to say that I'm scared, even though I keep telling myself I'll be fine. The Peanut will be fine. *Yet, I still can't write the words.*

After hearing about the traumatic blood loss Shelly and Naomi experienced, I feel like my heavy episodes paled in comparison. Standing up to have a morning pee, more amniotic fluid trickles away from The Peanut's lungs and into the sanitary napkin. Knowing what is leaving my body always makes me cringe a little.

After my brief flirt with being vertical, I return to bed and turn on the television. The headline kicks me directly in the uterus. A passer-by found a newborn girl abandoned in an outdoor stairwell. The street shares my name. Infanticide could be the only goal.

"What the fuck!" The anger I restrained towards Bruce explodes at the inanimate box. Fate taunts me. A woman throws away her child when I'm fighting unknown forces to keep mine.

Last night, I watched *Happy Feet*. It took me fifteen minutes to recover from Hugh Jackman's line, "No matter what, never drop your egg."

I imagine this infant laying on the hard landing, the bitter cold slowly claiming her limbs. Her voice, muffled by the kiss of concrete on her blueing lips, winds up the stairwell for help.

It's not the first of such stories I've heard. Nor, I know, will it be the last. Human frailties can lead us into such dark places.

My need to emote to Bruce overwhelms my earlier righteous defiance. I walk to the living room window anxious to share my maternal distress with him. The cleared driveway lies next to the snowy lawn. My temper fades. Life isn't always this black and white.

What circumstances did this mother endure that she (and the father?) felt condemning her baby to die was her only answer? No parent in their right mind could intentionally be that cruel, not in an age of people desperately seeking babies for adoption. *Could they?*

If it is true that we choose our parents, then perhaps this is why The Peanut chose us – because we'll fight for him. So many people already love The Peanut, are rooting for his success and want him to fight as much as we do even though he's not part of the world yet.

I place my hand over my baby. *I've loved you before you were conceived, Peanut. Although I can't wait to see you, please take your time to come out and say hello. Mummy's not going anywhere.*

CHAPTER 3

FEBRUARY 22, 2008

The monotonous call bell sings from the nursing station down the hall. It is exactly as I remember it from my early nursing career at Mt. Sinai. I count the number of electronic summons until someone answers it. Counting doesn't help put me to sleep.

The child I refused to give up five weeks ago is alive and moving. I won't do anything to jeopardize that. We met Dr. Finnegan, a high risk obstetrician a few weeks ago and I insisted that he hospitalize me when I reached 24 weeks of pregnancy. If The Peanut comes now, they will help him survive.

Yesterday, the drawn curtains of my semi-private hospital room nearly touched the bed. On one side of the eight by ten foot space, an over-the-bed table butted against a small bedside dresser. Bruce banged his knees when he sat in the chair next to me. He'd be in the bed if the space was any smaller.

Bruce departed shortly after we consumed a take-out supper on our laps, leaving me to stare at the lifeless beige walls and curtains. I kept my pessimism at bay with the routines of the evening shift nurse. She arrived for her assessment, struggling to get the blood pressure cuff on wheels to my arm. I didn't tell her I'm also a nurse.

Around ten o'clock, she came in for another peek at me. She met Spineless Me blubbering into the pillow I brought from home.

"Why are you crying?" I thought of the teaching videos modelling appropriate nursing communication.

You should say, "Tell me what is upsetting you."

Shut up Analytical Me.

The last few weeks have made me feel atypically anti-social. Before my water broke, Bruce and I hosted a New Year's Eve party so we could see the friends we hadn't been able to see in the previous weeks. I didn't know it was the last time I'd see most of them before I was hospitalized.

"I miss home."

She broke another rule of therapeutic communication 101 when she said, "You shouldn't worry about that now."

I'm in a different room tonight, vacuous in comparison to last night's curtained box. My nurse is the same. I want to "do over" the entire conversation with her:

Why are you crying? I miss the kisses Bruce gave me on the arm during the night last night whilst he was sleeping. He wasn't even aware that he was doing it. I barely woke up to feel them.

Why are you crying? My brain tugs on my heart strings when I wonder if my little Peanut will grow into a beautiful, intelligent little hellion.

Don't worry. Do you realize that I'm so scared deep down in my soul that I could lose the child I struggled to conceive?

I won't do it though. My aim is to be the model patient, not the model bitch. At least I'm not crying. That's a first for at least the last few days.

The Peanut is active tonight. The change to a private room and my routine ultrasound earlier today contribute to my calmer mood. The Peanut moved so much they couldn't measure him properly. His femur size is a week larger than average, his head is down and all the structures, both his and mine, look good.

I saw him practice breathing. It was marvellous to watch his chest move as it should despite my lack of measurable fluid pockets. Yesterday, I received the first injection of surfactant, a chemical which goes into his lungs to stop them from sticking together.

Best of all, The Peanut is one pound eleven ounces, officially big enough to resuscitate when he's born.

I get another thump from my tenant. Maybe The Peanut is having a temper tantrum because he's used to hearing Daddy's voice between ten o'clock and midnight. At home, Bruce spoke directly to my uterus each night, saying "keep peeing" and "stay inside Mummy." And always, Daddy loves you."

Kick.

Yes, child of mine, I hear you. Put down "Harry Potter" and go to bed. I set aside the world that mends broken people with mere words and the wave of a wand. *Oh that I could wave a hand over my belly and make things better for you, my Peanut.*

Poke.

I love you too.

My eyelids fly open, the dim light under the doorway hazy without my glasses. No one opened the door, so why am I awake? I peel the dampened night shirt away from my back. I turn over on the plastic mattress and kick off the blankets.

Then I feel the cause of my wakefulness. It rends the one flag of hope that I've waved proudly each week. The uterine cramping that woke me squeezes at my pelvis. Until now, my bleeding was painless. No pain, no miscarriage. *I can deal with this. It's mild. Let it ride.*

Rocking gently side to side doesn't make the ache go away. I admit defeat and notify my nurse. I draw my knees up slightly, guarding myself as I press the red button tied to the side rail.

One bing, two bings, three... I count patiently. *Where else am I going to go?*

"Don't worry" nurse enters the room. I hope she doesn't mistake this (ouch) pain for Anxious Me. I tell her about the pain that woke me just past 4:00 a.m., ten minutes ago.

"How many minutes between the cramps?"

Minutes between? No, I'm not... This can't be labour.

"It's constant. About a three out of ten but getting worse," I volunteer, anticipating her questions.

"Well, constant cramping isn't usually an indicator of going into early labour, but I will page the OB resident and tell her what's going on."

The nurse departs to notify the physician scheduled to deliver tonight's babies. She'll return with the equipment she needs to assess me and The Peanut, including his heart rate. That rapid whoosh-whoosh is the most thrilling sound for a mother. It's a highlight of my day.

I reach for the phone and flinch with a sharp pang. *It's too early baby, stay inside, you're not ready to come out yet. Please.*

Hearing the dial tone stops me. My mind struggles to remember. Is Bruce working this morning or is he coming here? My concept of days and weeks has been completely disrupted since I went on bed rest. The most noteworthy differences during the procession of days is the amount of blood and fluid I've lost.

After I press the first three numbers to reach our home, I pause again. *What am I going to tell him?*

Two days ago, Ontario celebrated its first Family Day holiday. I try not to think about it with bitterness. If my child is born now and doesn't survive, the holiday meant to celebrate families will always remind me how I was unable to create my own.

I hang up the phone before "Don't worry" nurse returns.

Once hooked up to the fetal and uterine monitor, she can't find the heartbeat. My heart fails. I haven't felt The Peanut move since I went to bed. Constant uterine contractions register on the monitor.

But, where are you Peanut?

An unexpected over-tightening of my anal sphincter deepens

my frown and I have to shift my hips to make it ease off. The action disrupts her search pattern. I look out the window, unable to see any stars in the city's over-lit night sky.

Please, Peanut.

The monitor spits out a ticker tape of my muscular activity. That uplifting whoosh-whoosh-whoosh continues to evade the nurse.

Thump-Kick.

In that action, there's a surge of relief.

The Peanut pushes off the probe just as "Don't worry" finds his heartbeat.

A resident physician comes in minutes later, but the pain is starting to ease. So too, is my worry. She suggests that I'm experiencing uterine irritability. She details multiple causes: the bleeding, fetal movement and growth, or infection.

With a hole in the amniotic sac, The Peanut's meager household is exposed to the normal bacteria of the vaginal canal. Even though I had antibiotics and avoided sex, there's a daily risk of infection.

"Your temperature's normal, your heart rate at baseline, and nothing seems amiss with Baby's heart," she continues. "I don't think Baby's in any distress. I'm not going to do an internal exam, because it may introduce bacteria. Of course, if something changes in your symptoms we'll re-examine you." She offers me morphine as both analgesic and smooth muscle relaxant.

I don't take it. I'd rather have the magic wand.

FEBRUARY 26, 2008

Today is a day for celebration, but neither Bruce nor I feel like celebrating. It's his birthday. We're cooped up in the hospital not wanting to be here, with no desire for the alternative.

I hear his characteristic jingle-step as he approaches the

room with a pocket full of change and a box of Tic Tacs. He's been in the maternity unit's kitchenette warming up dinner. "Fresh from the oven!" We try to remain jovial, pretending that sharing a re-heated supper on hospital over-bed tables as I lie in bed is as appealing as fine dining at one of our favourite restaurants. Bruce snuck in a beer as consolation. I'm concerned that the nurses will either make him get rid of it, or ban him from spending the night in the adjacent bed.

I'm tired of eating reclined and long for a proper chair. We're pleased that the cramping of last week didn't come back. The bleeding returned today, but I haven't the heart to tell him. When he goes to sleep at home he says goodnight to The Peanut and I, telling his child to behave for me and the doctors.

Ours was a random meeting in an online Scottish chat room in 2001. We grew our friendship through emails and hand-written letters, music mixes and token gifts. I sent him a packet of cookies when he wrote that his mouth watered after reading about my baking. The cookies were stale by the time they reached him in Scotland weeks later.

I'd sit on the bus or subway to work, scratching out thoughts along the bumpy surfaces. When I returned home from a twelve hour day shift, I eagerly read his letter before unpacking my work bag. Over time, our letters of daily life conveyed a sense of caring for each other's well-being, and of looking forward to our next interaction.

It's safe to say that I was fond of Bruce before I spoke to him on the phone months after that first email. Writing remained our predominant means of communication, mysterious and charming. After nearly a year, Bruce visited me in Toronto. Our relationship blossomed. We married in the summer of 2005.

As we eat in silence, I wonder if I would ever go back in time and change the outcome of that first visit. In the last few months, I've felt like he unknowingly agreed to take a damaged wife. Since being imprisoned in bed, I've seen Bruce become more and more unsettled. He hasn't seen much of the friends he has in Canada in last couple of months. Most of his support system lives overseas.

At eight, while we watch a DVD, a young doctor walks in. He speaks so quickly that I don't catch his name.

He's a neonatologist, the kind of doctor who will look after The Peanut when he is born. I've still not told Bruce I peeked at an ultrasound report and I know the Peanut is a boy. Again, the doctor bluntly delivers possible outcomes.

"There are four things that can happen at birth: the baby might take a breath and be fine, but given the oligohydramnios, this is a remote possibility." His next words strip away this layer of hope: if The Peanut breathes on his own, the pressure changes in his lungs and circulatory system could kill him.

"Baby might not breathe, in which case we'll resuscitate him to try and stimulate his breathing." The doctor leans against the wall as though the weight of what comes next might push him over. If they use a ventilator to help The Peanut breathe, it could damage his lungs, or change the pressures so drastically that he could have chronic lung disease.

The Peanut might not survive the attempt at resuscitation. *I don't need to know how many ways my newborn baby can die.*

I cannot bring myself to voice the words. Bruce remains quiet, reddened eye with tears about to burst their banks. I wonder if my stoic hero will be the first of us to crack tonight.

"Or the intubation and ventilator will work just fine and we'll leave it in until Baby's able to breathe without it."

The doctor recounts the risks associated with premature birth. He perfunctorily lists the problems we heard before: brain damage, disability, autism, learning disorders, organ dysfunction, cerebral palsy and more. His statistics are no less grim.

Remember, Shelley's daughter has none of these.

"There is good news." He tucks his hands casually into his jeans. "Babies do exponentially better week by week after 28 weeks of gestation." I have four weeks to go until The Peanut gets there.

Bruce seeks clarification on a couple of points. I don't pay attention to them. There's little more I want to learn tonight.

I turn my mind inwards willing my child to stay protected and happy until a distant 35 weeks, what our specialists commonly refer to as "early term." *Then you'll be in the clear my little love.* Babies born less than 37 weeks are premature by definition.

My thoughts return to the men as the doctor leaves, wishing Bruce a happy birthday. Bruce closes the door, firmly pushing it shut.

"Happy fucking birthday." He can't veil his sarcasm. "What the hell is happy about this birthday?" Birthdays are important to Bruce. He sits on the opposite bed. "I feel sick to my stomach."

Bruce has never dealt with this much stress before. The tears trickle down slowly, showing their strength as they resist gravity.

"I'm sorry, honey, I didn't know he was coming in today."

"It's not your fault." He stands up, going to the window, staring out at the emptying street. "Here's a great birthday present for you; let me tell you the number of ways your child can die or be disabled for life." His voice cracks a little. I know he's trying not to lose his temper.

We developed a pattern of coping during this trying pregnancy. When I'm stressed out or crying, he's the strong one. Generally speaking, that's most of the time. Sometimes he gives me his typical "there's nothing we can do about it so don't worry" speech. At other times, he just lets me get through the uncontrollable worry until I'm numb again. Most days it's numbness which surrounds me.

However, when Bruce's vulnerability cannot be ignored, I

try to remember that I don't always have to be the centre of our drama. Even though I'm feeling horrible about what the doctor said, I don't tell him. He already knows it.

I also don't know what to say to him to help him feel better. I can't say "don't worry" because that would be hypocritical. I fret about The Peanut all the time.

The night nurse enters for her evening assessment. Bruce wipes his eyes when she asks him if he'd like to hear his child's heartbeat. His temper's flash point passes. He confides that he snuck in a beer, so if the room smells of alcohol he's to blame. Looking at him, she lets him off the hook.

Alone, we discuss The Peanut's future. There is little we can do to plan for all the potential outcomes. Bruce points out that he'll be happy with the magic 28th week point.

"You can't expect more than that," he states softly.

"Why not? Isn't hope what's keeping us here?" I rant out the frustrations I'd restrained so well. Salt trails cover my face again. Bruce kneels down next to me, his hand on The Peanut.

"I need you not to cry because I need you to be strong, so I can be strong for you. I can't do this if you are breaking down. This situation makes me feel helpless. I'm emotionally spent, Lesley."

Self-Pitying Me insists that she needs to express herself but the look of sorrow on Bruce's face stuffs a sock in her mouth. He speaks to the small bump that is his child.

"Don't listen to the doctors. You're a fighter and they'll see how strong you are when you're born. I love you my little Peanut."

Fatigue wrestles us into separate beds, the movie forgotten. *You are so far away.* My tears drop onto my pillow as I listen to Bruce falling asleep.

CHAPTER 4

MARCH 05, 2008

There aren't any Tibetan protestors in the wind tunnel below my window today. Grey-brown slush coats the sidewalks. Discovery Alley looks like it does much of the year, populated by a human ant-mill. The only people standing still are the smokers outside the hospital entrances.

I return to the abandoned laptop. One sentence claims the pixels: "This is a funny looking San Antonio." We planned to be on holiday this week. *This isn't much of a holiday.* I delete the start of the blog post.

My mind is a complete blank. My part-time blog, once a travel-oriented re-vamp of my online presence, has become a personal journal. I know people read it and I'm very conscious of how depressing my entries are. No one wants to read about sadness over and over.

What else do I have to offer?

Nothing has changed with The Peanut. He's still squashed in my uterus. My bleeding slowed again. There's no pain or fever. I have no amniotic fluid. Things are boringly status quo.

It's been weird trying to cope, knowing that The Peanut's birth might mean his death. Bruce pointed out that if we let every day be traumatic, we won't do well. He's smart like that sometimes. I'm less able to box it up so nicely. He knows that I can't turn off the crying completely, nor do I think he would expect that.

Seeing my weaknesses every day wears away at his defenses because he doesn't know what to do about it. Bruce said he was shaking with stress when he went to bed last night after work. I didn't like hearing that. He doesn't talk much when he goes home, which isn't like either of us. *There's nothing that can be done about it.*

I'm defiantly wearing the white yoga pants I would never wear in public. Today, I intended to be wholly optimistic for the first time since I was admitted; then my stream of consciousness gained access to a keyboard.

The truth is I still feel like crap, especially when I'm alone, which is most of the time. Even so, I couldn't imagine going through this without any support network, even if it just helps pass the time.

Jessica came with her seven year old son. He heard The Peanut's heartbeat and was afraid to touch me. Gillian, my cousin, chatted away one evening with me. My friend, and former colleague, Paul set me up with his DVD player and his infinite library of CDs. He visits me after work twice a week.

I don't tell visitors how lonely I am; or how scared. *They see me as the brave one.*

The afternoon my mother visited, I recklessly confessed to her about a miscarriage when I was a teen. I wonder if a small part of me wanted to stir up some excitement through her reaction. Oddly, she didn't make a big deal out of it, nor did she bring it up in later phone calls.

A physician from work, Merv, unexpectedly stopped by. We haven't socialized outside of work so it surprised me. Moreover, Merv's demeanor proved inspirationally philosophical.

He said that we, Bruce, The Peanut and I, have become part of people's lives, not for our friendship, but because we remind them of the strength and positivity that exists in the world; our struggle is meaningful to everyone. His words made me choke up in joy for the first time in ages.

It gave me the motivation to try and shape my remaining days here to my advantage. To that end, I organised an arm and leg massage from the hospital's Women's Wellness Program.

It was by no means like being in a spa, but it was heavenly!

The lady who gave me the massage shared the story of her brother, now forty years old, who was born at seven months gestation in Mexico. Her mother was told the baby would not survive, and that she would be best off going home without him. She refused. She brought her son home and placed him in a padded shoe box with a lamp overhead to keep him warm. She fed him milk by dripping it from a cloth. He survived, becoming the father of six children.

The sparse visits, emails and phone calls are mortar in the wall of protection around my heart. Encouraging stories are all around me, if I choose to look.

One of my best friends, Michele, visited me with her newborn baby. Seeing her, I burst out in tears. Then I felt very selfish because her daughter was born early with intrauterine growth retardation. She spent time in the Level Two Special Care Nursery because she was 32 weeks old but sized more like 28.

I could blog about these people who have made ripples in my pond. Click. Click. Clack. Backspace repeatedly. Nothing worthy of reading ends up on the electronic page.

I'm scared I made the wrong decision. Is that the writer's block I can't break?

I want to believe that despite the fight The Peanut has ahead, everything will work out in the end. But I have images of a limp little body and funereal services invading my brain. Self-Pity Me is out in full force today asking, *Why me?*

I wish I could find the positive woman Merv left here. The difficulty in finding Optimistic Me could have something to do with the recent birth of Regina's daughter.

This hospital keeps us high risk preggos on the seventh floor, separate from the tenth floor mothers whose babies aren't expected to cause any problems.

On the seventh floor, my fellow perinatal inmates range from women having multiples, uncontrolled preeclampsia, or the dispiritingly named incompetent cervix, among other problems.

Two nights ago I met Regina through her roommate Larissa. Within moments of meeting Larissa on the elevator, she invited me to order pizza with herself and Regina.

I've had a few of those "So, what are you in for?" conversations with other seventh floor mothers, usually in the elevator on the rare occasion I travel downstairs. I don't like being upright because fluid still leaks out. That day, Bruce coaxed me to get up and stretch my legs when he couldn't be with me to make me do it.

"You have to meet her," Larissa said. "Regina's water broke early. This is her first pregnancy too. She's been here a couple of days. It'll be a girls' night in to break up the boring routine of the hospital food."

Where Regina was thin and dark haired, Larissa was round and fair. Regina's large glasses and scraggly hair made her seem so fragile, I wondered if she'd be able to handle a full term birth. She didn't talk about her pregnancy and I didn't feel comfortable prying. She never mentioned the baby's father.

As we ate, Larissa spoke of her twin pregnancy. Regina nodded point by point as if hearing it again for the first time.

One of Larissa's placentas invasively inserted itself into caesarian scar tissue in her womb from a previous child. She was so uncomfortable that she needed morphine. The doctors plan to deliver her babies by C-section at 35 weeks.

"Even if they are born without complications, the twins will need time in the NICU to wean off of the morphine before I take them home," she said.

Larissa lived outside of Toronto and her husband stayed at home working and managing the household with their five other children, including another set of twins. Her tone quieted when she talked about her family. The separation hit her hard.

A few days after our hen party, Regina went into labour. Larissa asked me to accompany her to the delivery room. She heard that the baby didn't survive and wanted to check in on Regina. I didn't want to go because I was afraid I would jinx myself; I couldn't think of a valid excuse to get out of it. The dark room resembled a bedroom, with upholstered furniture juxtaposed to the hospital bed. Wrapped up in blankets, Regina looked like a swaddled baby herself. The added warmth did little to improve the pallor of her skin.

"I knew I wouldn't be able to keep the baby," she said, volunteering sensitive information. "There was this odor before the pain started. Like, you know, an infection or something. Then when the baby came out, it didn't cry." To my amazement, she planned on returning to work the next week.

If she had been crying, she hid the evidence. Emotions stirred inside me I couldn't control.

My child will breathe. I'm healthier than this woman.

I became judgemental of her situation, appearance and apparent lack a partner, as if those things contributed to the loss of her child.

I regret it now. Perhaps she did want to be pregnant as much as I do. Fate denied her the choice. I realize that my fear made me irrational against anything which paralleled her situation with mine.

Maybe it's the guilt of those thoughts and not my self-pity looming over me. Human complexity drove one woman to abandon Baby Angelica-Leslie in a stairwell. Regina may be sheltering herself from her loss in a better way than I ever could.

When my time comes, and The Peanut is torn from me, what will I do?

MARCH 09, 2008

I push rice around my plate, more to avoid eating in front of our friends from than from a dislike of the food, although the latter is equally true of tonight's meal. We found Joel and Jeny entering my room when we returned upstairs, Bruce matching my slower pace down the long hallway.

"Thank you for coming so soon after your loss. I know it can't be easy for you to be around pregnant women." The sudden wail of a newborn in another room interrupts Jeny's response.

They sit beside each other holding hands at the foot of my bed. Not yet recovered from her miscarriage, she looks like a Filipino Snow White.

Jeny was 17 weeks pregnant when she found out that for five weeks she unknowingly carried a dead fetus. She and Joel chose to deliver the baby naturally after an injection to induce labour. It wasn't supposed to work as fast as it did. Joel found her haemorrhaging and nearly unconscious on the bathroom floor. He saved his wife as he lost his child.

Joel squeezes her hand and says, "We had a ceremony with our Pastor and buried the baby privately last month." Jeny looks out the window and presses her lips together, not surrendering further details.

"People have asked us when we're going to try again, like the first baby didn't count," Joel says. The wrinkles to the corners of his eyes have deepened. "Or, they think they are helping by saying, 'You're young. You can have more kids'." Bruce swears under his breath.

"We've decided to file the things that some people say under the category of Not Helpful." Joel always had a knack for humour; it's now tempered with a wisdom I wish he didn't have to know.

Larissa walks into the room, announcing herself with

familiarity. She and I have daily contact now, especially when our husbands are absent. I guess she didn't expect to see Bruce today. The storm kept him away yesterday, much to my dismay.

"Hi. Sorry to interrupt. Lesley, I just wanted to know what happened to you yesterday with the bleeding and stuff. I came back in to see you after my kids left, but you were gone." Bruce offers up his perch on the adjacent bed. Jeny's eyes widen slightly at the size of Larissa's very pregnant belly.

Uterus Diva Me takes centre stage.

"The bleeding started up again," my ER nurse's eyes watch Jeny closely. "It was bad. And I had some pain too, like the uterine cramping I had last week. But I didn't think anything of it." I drink a mouthful of the lukewarm decaf tea from the coffee shop downstairs, my other big field trip of the week. "Even so, they took me to a case room to monitor The Peanut."

I addressed Larissa, "It's not like the nice room Regina had. It's only half the size of this room and no niceties. Not a favourable place to have a baby." Bruce stretches and yawns. It was another 5:00 a.m. start for him. He heard this story upon his arrival here when he finished work.

"After three hours, things improved with morphine and no baby came out. So, they sent me back and I finished the last *Harry Potter* somewhere around midnight." I avoid telling them about the return of the pain overnight.

"The Peanut is in the 80th percentile for his age and he has a femur the size of 29 week fetus even though he's only 26 weeks. I still don't have any fluid in there but man," I pause feeling the ache increase as the footballer kicks on cue, "can that kid connect with my abdominal wall!" I press my lower belly more firmly trying to ease the increasing discomfort.

"Are you OK?" Larissa surveys my face. *Obviously I'm not as good at hiding my discomfort as I thought.*

"Sitting up hurts a bit, that's all." Lying as I lie here.

Suddenly, the leisurely afternoon visit gets a spur of activity. Joel and Jeny leave, their dinner plans not yet sorted out. Bruce takes his vest from the closet and drapes it on the end of the adjacent bed, preparing to leave. Larissa says focused on me.

"I should head home soon too, sweetie. Another day shift tomorrow." He rearranges the vacant visitors' chairs as he talks, erasing evidence of the outside world.

"You know, Bruce, I've got a lot of experience with childbirth," Larissa says, facing him. "You shouldn't go home. I think Lesley's going into labour."

ORANGE
March 8 to April 1, 2008

CHAPTER 5

MARCH 09, 2008

Bruce stares at Larissa blankly. I catch my breath when a deep twinge hits. It diverts her attention back to me.

"Do you need something stronger for the pain?"

Shaking my head, I rub The Peanut. "No, not yet. I'm sure it will pass like the last time." I try to breathe through the pulling sensation in my abdomen. The blonde woman sets her shoulders and faces my husband, puppeteering his choices with her eyes.

"I wouldn't be surprised if you're going to be a father tonight. You should stay here." I hope he agrees with her, mostly because I don't want to go through another evening like yesterday without him.

Bruce checks his watch, reaches for his sleeveless jacket and then leaves it on the bed. He agrees to stay another twenty minutes. I picture Larissa wielding her unborn twins at him if he tries to leave. My internal laughter trips over the sharp spasms. I yelp in an adulterated wince.

"You see, Bruce, she's in pain. You really shouldn't go home," Larissa chastises her newly adopted husband-brother-child. I've lost count of how many admonishments this makes.

"I think I need the morphine." My eyes rise in apology to him. Bruce settles into the chair closest to my bed. Larissa beams triumphantly as I press the call bell.

Minutes later, analgesic received, an unfamiliar red haired obstetrician mutters from between my elevated knees.

"Your cervix is closed, so you aren't delivering right now," she says as she removes her sterile gloves with precision. This could be the scene in *Father of the Bride Two* when Steve Martin asks his wife's OB if she's old enough to be a doctor.

Mine tells me that she can't predict what is to come. Bruce holds my hand with a sweaty palm. I hear his stomach growl.

Larissa lets the ginger haired doctor corral her team out of the room before she returns to us, although I suspect that she's been waiting to hear what the doctor said.

"Bruce, I'm glad you're staying a bit longer." Her face is as bright as the light the doctor used for her exam. She resumes her supervisor's position on the bed next to mine.

With each parade of the stomping army in my belly, I'm unable to focus. Larissa compares it to the march of time on her wrist. There is a reprieve every ten minutes.

"When I get morphine, it doesn't take this long to kick in. You should be having some relief by now." The noises being made by my body reveal the truth about the failure of the analgesic. She stands up and confronts Control Freak Me. "I'm going to get your nurse."

"I wish Larissa would stop telling me not to leave," Bruce lowers his voice to the loud grumble he calls a whisper when she leaves the room. "I wasn't going anywhere."

"She means well, Brucie." I pat the bed, wanting him close. I haven't hugged him since he arrived. "I think she's being protective. You know..." Moaning steals my breath away.

Larissa returns, finding Bruce comforting me in his embrace. She informs us that she directed my nurse to come see me. Her own evening monitoring pending, she retreats to her room. Bruce's shoulders drop two inches.

Down the hall, the echo of my groan precedes its antecedent. Then I realize it's another woman crying out before me. I join her in a duet of agony. *She's the one in labour. Not me.*

Bruce spies on the other woman in labour being rolled down the hall when I call out to him in pain. Was that ten minutes? My nails leave marks in his skin.

"It hurts so much." My moaning rivals the death throes of

the proverbial fat lady. Bruce's blue eyes show me something that I don't want to know.

A Jamaican nurse named Rose enters. She's cared for me before. Rose stands with her hands on her hips.

"What's all the commotion goin' on in here, girl? I can hear you halfway down the hall." I start to explain my situation to her but cannot finish. I double over from the squeezing pain of my abdomen.

Her response is immediate. "You'll be needin' a doctor." The same too-young (*please-be-competent*) doctor returns, ginger hair pulled back in a pony tail, ready for business. She performs an internal exam using bulk gloves form the open box on the wall. *She isn't concerned about sterility.*

She yanks off the gloves saying, "Mr. and Mrs. Donaldson, you're going to have a baby tonight."

Bruce and I start crying. He leans down to kiss me. His tears taste the same as mine.

"No. No, it's too early!" *Was that him or me?* "Is there any way you can stop it?" The doctor shakes her head at my plea. If Bruce squeezes me any harder, I won't be able to breathe.

The doctor comes to my side, a delicate hand on my knee. "I'm sorry. I can't. I'll do an ultrasound in the room to make sure the baby is positioned properly. If the baby is breech or side-lying, you'll need a C-section."

Bruce buries his face in my belly. His voice chokes as he says to his unborn son, "You show them! You show them!" He kisses my forehead. His eyes are red and wet. *You remind me of my husband.* Any stereotype of a British stiff upper lip never prepared me for this image. I've never seen him cry before.

The fingers of fate grab at my uterus. It's almost nine. Panic rises. It occurs to me that I don't know how to breathe properly. I didn't take any pre-natal preparations. I watched a delivery when I was a nursing student and nearly fainted.

What was I thinking getting pregnant?

The doctor's ultrasound gives me one last two-dimensional black and white look at The Peanut. He's head down, read to come out. The next time I see him will be in full colour.

Nurses transport me by stretcher to the case room. Mary, the labour and delivery nurse takes over my care. She looks like the Shirley Jones of the Viking era, with wild sun kissed hair. I discard my dignity as well as my blood soaked underwear, and transfer from the red-smeared linens of the stretcher to the delivery bed.

Bruce squeezes past it into an adjacent chair. His knees scuff the side of the bed. Mary prepares me for her portion of tonight's staging of *Singing in the Pain*.

"I don't know what I'm supposed to do," I tell her. She looks confused. "For the delivery. I studied L&D at nursing school and passed, but I have no idea what to do."

"You be the mom. I'll be the nurse." I relinquish my brain to Mary, my mind's eye seeing her as the assertive pilgrim-midwife calling out for hot water and clean blankets.

We arrived here at ten o'clock. At some point between the clenching waves in my belly, an anaesthesiologist consults me for an epidural. Although this is a teaching hospital, lumbar puncture is one procedure for which I've refused students. My spinal cord is too valuable to be a teaching tool.

She begins with a routine investigation into my health history. Every three minutes I can't speak because of the uncontrollable pain. It lasts for one and a half minutes each time. After several interruptions, the doctor stands up.

"I'm just going to get you an epidural." It's the best information I've heard all day.

Fifteen minutes later, I'm pain free. The cord supplying the medication fentanyl juts out from my lower back but I ignore it. I also can't feel my legs.

"It's to be expected," explains Mary, her hands skillfully adjusting the multiple wires and lines. "And how's your pain?"

"I have some twinges on the left lower side." *Stick a fork in me, I'm done.* I wish my belly had the roundness of a roasted turkey.

"Those are your contractions my friend."

"Then, bring it on!" My teeth come out of hiding for the first time in hours.

Bruce and I enjoy a few minutes of solitude for the first time since Larissa realized my situation.

"You want to lie on my pillow in case you pass out?" I tease. He's notoriously squeamish about blood. There's a bit of colour back in his face. "You know, they can only handle two patients at a time, and I'm cooking the second."

"I'm not going to pass out," he responds with a derisive snort. I've taunted him about fainting before. His skin is getting thin. "You just do your job and don't worry about me." Bruce cups my face and kisses me. "I'm proud of you."

"OK kids, that's what got you here in the first place," Mary breezes in, flipping over the tracer output from the fetal monitor. "And it looks like you need to get this baby out."

Bruce looks at her with concern.

"The Baby's heart rate is going up during your contractions. That means it's getting tough for Baby in there, especially without any fluid to help. I'm going to page the doctor and you're going to push."

Push? But I'm so comfortable.

"But I don't have any rectal pressure or feel the need to push." Tidbits of my labour and delivery training trickle into my head.

"That's because of the epidural. It's great for dealing with pain, but it can't do the work for you." She calls out into the hallway looking for assistance, but no boiled water or blankets.

Mary coaches me as I bear down. The word "push" comes out with the pace of a dragon boat drummer on crack.

How many times can a person say Push in one breath?
I crush Bruce's hand demanding this point of contact to give me the strength I need to move the unseen life in my body. He leans down to take a school-boy peek between my legs, seeing only blood. He doesn't faint.

Mary holds my right knee up to my chin. *Where did that nurse holding up my left leg come from?* Mary and her machines tell me when to bear down and when to breathe.

A male obstetrician enters the room with his junior self in tow. *Of course it would be a handsome student staring up my V-jay-jay.*

"I was starting to think I was going to have to catch this one for you Dr. Hamilton," Mary says, elbowing the older man in the arm. I'm sure her hands are more than capable.

"Surgical delivery across the hall folks. Couldn't be helped," he says at my feet. The hospital phone tucked in his waistband rings as he dons a pair of gloves. Mary picks it up.

"Is that them paging me to come to this delivery?" She nods at him, her hair jumping up and down like school kids at an ice cream truck. "Tell them I'm not going to go!"

Our laughter is the last singularly identifiable sound in the room. What follows is a cacophony of instructions: ring-side coaching from Mary, "Give it all you can!"; the doc crooning "Good! Good!"; and Bruce alternating between the schmeck of a kiss and whispering, "I love you."

Somewhere between my legs a tiny body emits the quiet, gurgling cry of the baby whose lungs were not expected to work.

"Time of birth 12:30," the doctor states to Mary.

Dr. Hamilton holds him up above my pelvis. My son opens his eyes and looks at his parents. His tiny arms and legs wave about seeking comfort in this strange cold world. Blood fills his mouth. *Suction! Suction!* Emergency Nurse Me kicks into gear.

There is no offer for me to hold him. A respiratory therapist carries my swaddled child to the door, pausing slightly before she dashes across the hall to the resuscitation room.

"And what did we have, doctor?" Mary now turns her coaching skills on her colleague.

"Yes. It's a boy." He looks up between my lifeless legs with a sheepish grin.

Then, my son is gone. For the second time tonight, Bruce and I cry in stereo. My arms hold the only male in my life they can reach.

Twenty minutes later, Bruce gets a rare invitation to see his son before the intravenous lines are inserted. My incapacitated legs make it impossible for me to leave.

I remain blissfully trapped there when the red headed obstetrician returns, a pinched look replacing her earlier smile. She managed one of the other deliveries and now attends for my post-partum care.

"You haven't delivered your placenta and your cervix is starting to close," she states. If they can't remove it, I might rupture and bleed to death, or retain the so-called products of conception and develop an infection.

She attempts manual manipulation as Mary stands beside her, her curls hypnotically swaying as she shakes her head.

The doctor determines she needs to open my cervix and scrape the placenta out. We nearly run over Bruce as they wheel me to the surgical suite across the hall.

"His entire fist held my finger tip," he says after blowing his nose into his handkerchief. It's the first time father and son connected. "I'll never forget it. They say he's a fighter. He's been pushing away the wires on his body and pulling tubes out of his nose and mouth."

The surgical doors open, flooding light into the hallway. Bruce stares when he realizes we are not returning to my room. Then, the doors close and he is gone.

The obstetricians below my waist speak in hushed and pressured tones trying to defuse my time bomb without knowing which wire to cut. I struggle to lean my head up.

"Do what you have to do down there. It's OK. My son is alive. Can I help in some way? After all, I am a nurse." *Is that the anaesthetic talking?* The anaesthesiologist tells me in her maternal tone that tonight I'm off duty.

Mary appears out of nowhere with an equally stern don't-move look upon her face.

"Your placenta isn't coming out, my friend. That cervix has just slammed shut and the oxytocin we gave you isn't helping move it along."

I'm physically numb and oblivious to the amount of haemorrhaging down below. "This is more activity than my lower body has seen in months."

Conscious that I've been here longer than a hospital-style few minutes, I ask Mary to check on Bruce. It must be torture for him to have the two people he loves the most squirreled behind closed doors in potentially disastrous medical circumstances.

In a room with wires and monitors, my son shows nurses his strength; another room holds my husband who has been stronger today then I've ever seen him. All I know at this moment is love for my boys.

CHAPTER 6

MARCH 10, 2008

The sky through the window is brighter today. Grey winter clouds, such a familiar view, were chased away by Apollo heralding the arrival of my son. The words saunter gaily around my brain. My son, Torran. I can't sleep because I'm smiling too much.

The feeling in my legs slowly returned. My toes wiggle at my command. Movement has never been so hard. Bruce dozes in the adjacent bed. Yesterday demanded 24 hours from him, something his body isn't used to. I blow the father of my son a kiss in the growing morning light.

Bruce was the last piece of my life puzzle and the most difficult to both conceptualize and find. I didn't want to give my children the life I knew, caught between parents.

My parents separated when I was six, I think. I went from being Daddy's Little Girl to Mom's Defensive Boudica. My relationship with my father disintegrated over the years; Mom and I have our own tribulations.

When I was fifteen, a family court judge attempted to salvage a relationship between father and daughters. It didn't work. By then, I was as opinionated about the world as I was ready to conquer it. My father didn't change his approach either. The awkwardness continues today. My sister reached out to him when she went to University. She reconciled with him and wants me to do the same.

"I can't go through this and deal with him at the same time," I told her when she asked if I wanted to tell our father. I'm not changing my mind now that Torran is alive. Protectiveness about my son trumps any guilt about avoiding my father.

A soft tapping at the door announces a nurse's entry into the room. She introduces herself and begins the post-delivery assessment. Bruce lifts his head, looking worried. I tell him to go back to sleep. He's not needed yet.

"Are you planning on breast feeding or formula?" The mantra "breast is best" comes to mind - I recall that much from nursing school.

"Breast feeding." I choose breast feeding to start because I've not organised an alternative.

"Great. Your son won't have the reflexes to feed by mouth right now, but we can store your breast milk in the freezer in the Unit. The nurses will feed it to him through a tube until he develops the skill to take it orally." She returns with a piece of equipment mounted on a rolling stick and an armful of plastic accoutrements.

I'm glad Bruce is sleeping through this part. The breast pump machine is compact, with tubes that run from two funnel shaped cones to a collection bottle. The nurse tells me how the siphoning process works, helping me hold the plastic cones on my breasts.

She turns on the pump and it sucks my nipples into the straight part of the funnel, filling it completely. The alien looking tissue expands and contracts in unison with the machine's suction. I never thought my nipples could get so big. Strings of electricity dash upwards from the areolas as my mammary glands activate.

"Sometimes it takes a while for mothers to get any... whoa!" Multiple thin streams of cream coloured liquid explode from my body and coat the lower part of the tube in milky droplets. "I don't think I've seen it happen that quickly before. Good for you!" I laugh nervously, unsure of what I did to deserve the kudos. the nurse leave me with my first official job of motherhood: being milked like a cow.

Bruce rolls over, admitting that he was awake but didn't want to interrupt. He watches me with a goofy grin on his face, sniggering.

"You've got a nice pair of baps there Missus," he gestures towards me, raising his eyebrows suggestively.

"If you don't stop giggling, I'll do it to you." The suction causes an unpleasant friction on my nipples.

He closes his mouth, but his abdomen quakes. Bruce kisses the top of my head. Without a baby inside me, I'm not afraid of sitting up, but my back hurts from the epidural. I tilt my chin up in response. Our mouths meet softly. Prickly stubble on his chin presses into me.

"I'm sorry that I was mad at you for not coming on Saturday. I didn't like being here without you."

"Forget about it." His lips find my forehead. "It hasn't even crossed my mind." Bruce looks at my chest and wiggles his eyebrows at me. "Just keep doing a good job." I'd swat him in the arm, but cannot let go of the plastic cones.

Within ten minutes, the machine sucks me dry. It grosses me out that the most precious thing I can give my son, and the first thing to go smoothly with my pregnancy, is in a collection cup I usually see full of urine or feces.

My mother and sister stand holding each other next to the incubator in the Neonatal Intensive Care Unit. The high pitched beeps of the machines around us barely register on my ears. My son's ventilator is quiet. His vital data registers on a monitor above his plastic womb.

Tears threaten their eyes, which moments ago shone with excitement. Sitting, I can't hug them without making them strain down to reach me, so I don't bother. I have the use of my legs back, but I nearly collapsed going to the bathroom. Mom and Jessica forced my ghostly body in a wheelchair.

With all the hospital staff coming and going, I still haven't slept properly. I'm commanding myself to sit upright and keep myself alert. My back ache prevents me from giving in to a slouch.

"He looks good, Les," my mother glances at me. *When did she start to look her age?* Her tone confesses that she expected something worse. I can't make eye contact with my mother for too long or else I'll start crying. I return my gaze to her hand pressing against the plastic wall of the incubator.

During the night, Bruce and I visited Torran. I knew what to expect; I tried to prime them, but it didn't help. We lifted the blanket covering one side, otherwise they'd be looking at a large plastic box with a giraffe blanket lying over top of it. The nurses told us that the brightness in the room bothers the baby's eyes. At 26 weeks and six days gestation, a baby should be in complete darkness.

Torran's arm twitches, giving my sister a start. Torran hasn't moved much. He likes to rest his arm above his head, without the constricting uterus around him. The nurses reposition him every few hours to prevent pressure sores. They don't introduce their hands into his plastic home unless they need to. Germs make nurses in this unit very nervous. Physical manipulation also induces stress in his fragile body.

Torran stops moving erratically and both women's shoulders relax a few centimetres.

Moisture accumulating on the inside of the dim incubator forms a thin rivulet. There are a slew of wires on Torran's tiny body. A flat silver temperature probe, slightly larger than a quarter, adheres to his abdomen. A large foam block secures an intravenous line to his arm. It would be a ridiculously funny prop in another circumstance. Another IV comes out of his navel. A rolled up blanket forms a positioning cushion around his body hugging him like my arms ache to do.

Torran doesn't look that much different from three o'clock in the morning, when Bruce and I first visited him in the resuscitation room. Cleaner, perhaps. Dried blood hides in the crevices of his limbs.

At least the swelling on his eyelids has gone down now that he's started to pee. Earlier, he looked like he'd been punched in the face. His face and body still appear too round.

A line of pink plastic tape straddles his face, securing the breathing tube in his nose. The ventilator vibrates his chest as it blows air in and out, giving him precious puffs of life.

His nurse, Melissa, comes to check on us. I know there are only supposed to be two visitors at a time but I didn't want to be alone in my room. With my family here, I sent Bruce home to rest and refresh. I portrayed myself as a confident woman for a picture during my first visit to the NICU, giving two thumbs up at Torran's incubator. My body lied for the photo.

My mother can't contain herself any longer. "Can I please have a special Nana moment? I just want to touch him with my finger," she asks Melissa, a tear escaping down her cheek. I try to recall if I told her that we aren't supposed to touch Torran to reduce the risk of infection.

Before I can figure out how to deny her request without offending her, Melissa cautiously agrees if my mother cleans her hands thoroughly first. I let it slide. After all, I kissed his hand last night. How much more damage will be wrought by her finger?

Jessica adjusts the colourful flowers on the windowsill. A CON-GRATULATIONS sign rests in the middle of the vase. A single card stands beside it. Mom sits between the hospital beds in the wheelchair I abandoned, drinking a coffee. They've both recovered from visiting Torran, sniffles and drippy eyes now firmly dried.

"Why did you name him Torran?" my mother asks.

"I wanted Graeme, but Bruce doesn't like that name. The name is Scottish. It means "from the rocky hills", a Tor being a rock in Scotland. His middle names are Bruce Peter Victor. Bruce and Peter follow Bruce's tradition of naming after fathers. I wanted Valarian, Latin for victorious. Bruce wouldn't go for that, so I got Victor instead."

She asks how long Torran's going to be in the hospital. I shrug.

"It depends. A social worker came in today." Her eyebrows pinch together. "Oh don't worry; it wasn't to take him away. They meet with parents of micro-preemies to tell them about the support programs. She said that babies his gestational age often go home before their due date. We could be transferred to a Level Two Special Care Nursery closer to home when he reaches 35 weeks." The hospital started discharge planning when I arrived in February. *There's only so much room in this inn too.*

"Like the one Simon was in?" Jessica sits in a chair at the end of bed tapping on her Blackberry. My sister's son was born five weeks early from a spontaneous rupture of membranes. At the time, Simon was the smallest human being I'd ever seen. He weighed four pounds and spent some time in the hospital learning feeding reflexes and gaining weight. I felt like I would crush him when I held him during my first visit.

"You know, when I was in the hospital with Simon they told me that holding him against my skin helps with controlling breathing and heart rates. It's called a Kangaroo hold. Are you going to do that?"

"I sincerely doubt they'll let me hold him while he's on the ventilator. I'm not even allowed to touch him much. Torran won't come out of the incubator for several weeks. Kangaroo care isn't a possibility right now." Fatigue more than anger prompts my direct stare and curt words. My chest tightens, anticipating a challenge. The comparison between our children is inevitable. Torran weighs almost half that of his cousin's birth weight, and is significantly earlier in gestation.

"Well, for later, I mean, obviously," she replies, quickly casting her eyes back down to her phone. She takes a breath as if to say something. The vents in the windowsill blow the card over. She stands to correct it.

Not one to be daunted by details, Jessica continues on another line of thought. "The wife of my friend gave birth early and even though they monitored the baby closely, the doctors failed to catch that he had a heart murmur. Apparently, it's common for early deliveries."

I interrupt her before she can continue farther.

"Jes, I know you have Torran's best intentions at heart, but don't tell me everything you know that can happen to my son." She doesn't look away from me this time. "He barely came away from being born. Can you please, just try not to be so intelligent for the next little while and keep that kind of information to yourself? I can only deal with so much at a time. Bruce and I have every confidence that they will be monitoring him closely for potential problems." I see her teeth grit ever so slightly as she looks through me.

"I need a cigarette," my mother announces implying that Jessica needs to take her downstairs in the wheelchair. Mom probably thinks she's helping to prevent an argument. However, neither my sister nor I smoke, so I'm not sure which situation would cause Jessica more irritation.

Undeterred by the interruption, I raise my eyebrows at my sister, silently demanding a response. Before she gets up to begrudge our mother with her request, Jessica dips her chin, her lips pursing together very slightly.

CHAPTER 7

MARCH 12, 2008

The hospital was never this quiet at 4:00 a.m. At home, there are no car horns bleating from the street below, nor any forlorn call bells in the hallway. Even Bruce's snoring respects the reverence of this hour.

My heart searches for the shattering noise I long to hear. No baby cries.

I walk to the far end of the bungalow and dial the hospital. The portable phone is almost as long as the boy who should be at home disrespecting the quiet.

The faceless nurse I met at shift change tells me Torran is "fine."

I have to probe her for further details.

Yesterday I met a mother who said, "Oh, you're a nurse, then being here should be easy for you." She was wrong. My learning curve may be faster than the average parent, but the NICU feels vastly different to my work environment. My mental checklist ticks off little boxes as the nurse speaks.

Is he breathing? Torran's on the ventilator. His oxygen and carbon dioxide levels still fluctuate. He's retaining carbon dioxide and has acidic blood. They're using nitrous oxide to help him breathe (*but he's not laughing*).

What is his oxygen level? The team maintains Torran's oxygen level between 84-94%. It helps prevent the eye damage which results from the gas. I associate those numbers with a chronic smoker. I hope that Torran has Bruce's eyes, which are stronger than mine. My father gifted me with his severely myopic vision.

What about his jaundice? Torran's bilirubin levels are increasing because his liver isn't functioning well and his dietary intake is poor. They'll probably start him on phototherapy tomorrow. *Are you feeding him yet?* Since he hasn't made his first bowel movement, the meconium plug, he's still not allowed to have my breast milk.

Is his blood sugar under control? His blood sugar is high. He has an intravenous line for the insulin drip which regulates the sugar level. I think of the heel pokes for repeated blood sampling which macerate the bottom of his five centimetre long feet. *They're going to run out of places to prick him.*

And then, there's that other issue.

What about his head? Torran's head remains swollen. His fontanelles, the soft spots at the front and back of his head bulge slightly, with widening spaces between his skull bones.

Given his appearance and the significant 26 unit drop in his hemoglobin level in the first day, Bruce and I anticipate confirmation that he has a bleed in his brain.

But he's fine.

Earlier today we arrived during the head ultrasound. The doctors bumped it up a day because of the falling hemoglobin.

Torran's brain, as grainy as his pre-natal ultrasound, floated on the screen, the halves unequal. I don't know to read ultrasounds, but I do know both sides should be the same. I don't expect the news about the ultrasound to be good.

"Maybe the blood drop is from something else." Bruce insists on optimism. He wants to be a direct blood donor for Torran. Fathers are allowed to donate if they are compatible. Mothers can't because of the amount of blood lost during delivery.

"I feel useless. If it's the only thing I can do for our son then he can have as much as he wants." He is a blood type match for Torran and his sample lacks common viruses that would make him ineligible, including the Cytomegalovirus which exists in most fathers.

In the meantime, the team used an anonymous donor for

Torran's transfusion. We have to look beyond the risks; Torran's life is more important.

"Tell him that Mummy loves him." I stifle a cry into the phone before I press END. I'll never know if she'll actually do it.

I open the curtain and stare out the window, pumped milk on the table behind me. There isn't a single part of my face that turns upwards with happiness. I don't have a mother's glow; I have an "I'm so sorry, baby" shadow.

The memory of my arrival home without my child won't leave my mind. When the obstetrician came to assess me yesterday morning, she raised a concern about my low blood count. I bled a lot after Torran's delivery and the prolonged D&C to remove my placenta. I countered that if she wasn't going to give me a blood transfusion, there was no point in staying in hospital. The doctor relented and prescribed iron pills.

"After all, 86 isn't that low of a number," I rationalized to Bruce as we left the hospital, "so long as I'm not symptomatic." I didn't tell him that it was a bit difficult to breathe and my insides hurt. I believed my recovery was best achieved at home, even if it meant being farther away from Torran a day earlier than the doctors wanted. *Maybe they were right.*

I called my mother when we arrived home. "It's me. We're back." I sagged onto the edge of my bed for the first time in weeks. I didn't know which hurt more, my vagina, my back, or my swollen legs.

Listening in, Bruce started unpacking my bag of clothes from the hospital.

"Hi. How's the baby?" she responded. I gave her the summary from when we last saw Torran. "And how are you doing?"

Thoughts crashed around my brain.

"Lesley?"

"I can't hold my son," were the only intelligible words that came out of my mouth. Doubled over, arms clasped around my vacant belly, I let out long visceral moans between my sobs. As if from a distance, my mother said something. I was dimly aware of Bruce on the other side of the bed frozen in his own impotency.

That horrific wailing seemed to go on forever. It continues to haunt me. I've never seen an actress portray the same soul-crushing weep.

Having a super-preemie makes parents at risk for post-partum depression and post-traumatic stress disorder. So far, I've been able to recognize when I'm not able to handle a situation, like being at his bedside, and remove myself. *I wonder how long that's going to last?*

My family has never seen me so fragile. Raw weakness is not in my nature. I'm keenly waiting for the first day of Torran's medical stability and true emotional control. Right now, I feel edgy and weary. I reserve genuine smiles for Torran.

I open the fridge and make room for the expressed breast milk. At least that part is superb. My mammary chefs don't realize their client is on a diet. The nurses asked me to start freezing milk at home because there's already too much in their fridge.

The NICU Welcome binder beckons me from the coffee table as I pass through the living room. I caress the photo of Torran we tucked under the plastic cover. My hands feel the same thing when they touch the wall of the incubator. They long for so much more.

Torran has that adorable newborn factor, despite the tubes in his facial orifices, wires on his body, and intravenous lines in his limbs. *And the blood and bruising.*

The swelling that made his face look unusually round improved after he lost some of his birth weight. I wish I could kiss his tiny nose.

Torran already shows some personality. He's a little feisty, pulling at tubes and lines with his long wrinkled fingers. He always grips Bruce's finger tightly. Me, I'm just the lady who makes the milk and changes the diaper, so my squeezes aren't as good. I prefer laying my hand on the top of his head like the "how to interact with your preemie" instructions in the binder suggests. I can't stroke his abundant hair, because such actions irritate the babies.

Like Bruce, Torran prefers lying on his left side; it doesn't set off his oxygen as much. Tonight the nurses tried him on his stomach to clear gas in his belly. Nothing pinged, so he must enjoy it. If he lays like that for too long, however, he might lose the IV line in his navel.

Sometimes he opens his eyes and it looks like they move from Bruce to me and back. The weird thing is, I can't see any pupils. I gave birth to a Little Orphan Annie character. Eventually, his eyes will be blue, like ours.

Torran's face has adorable little movements. I lose time staring at him. I prefer the quizzical eyebrows to the frowning grump. He can't cry because of the ventilator tube in his nose and throat.

My finger traces the two dimensional image of Torran's wonderfully complex looking ears. Nurses fluff the squashed ears when they reposition him.

For infection control and to give him a rest, they aren't overdoing his handling. They changed their nursing schedule for Torran to match our planned visitation times. It means I can participate in his care. Being a nurse and demonstrating my confidence in the skills ensured me of that privilege. It's also good for Torran.

On Tuesday, I reached in to Torran's box to change a diaper and measure his temperature. At the end of the night, the nurse placed him flat in my hands whilst she reset the scale hidden under his bed. Torran was the most fragile, lightweight and precious package I could ever imagine.

He weighed 2.18 pounds or 990 grams, a decrease in birth weight from 2 pounds 5 ounces or 1048.9 grams. I have to start thinking in metric because that's what they use in the unit. It seems as foreign for infants as it is for lumber.

I nicknamed him The Blonde Sasquatch because of the light coloured lanugo, the fine hair all over his body. Torran's limbs can't straighten because my oligohydramnios gave him no room to move. We're told this will improve over time. If not, he'll have physiotherapy when he's full term. His right groin looked a little puffy, perhaps from a hernia.

I stand at the bedroom door and watch Bruce sleeping. The man I married is fantastic. Not only in the way he cares for me, but also in his participation of Torran's birth, letting himself bawl when he needed it, and in the amount of love he has shown for his baby boy.

Bruce told me that when he rode the public transit home the day Torran was born, he spent the entire fifty minute trip staring at the two pictures of Torran the nurses took after his birth.

They're still propped up at his bedside.

I'm proud of Bruce for overcoming his own squeamish medical issues. He's with his son every day. Bruce is very afraid of handling Torran because he is a self proclaimed clumsy person. He has no fear of reaching into the incubator and touching his little man. Torran's entire palm and fingers cup Bruce's fingertip.

I've told him that I appreciate him being at the hospital with me, even if he feels like he didn't do anything. I don't know how I could be able to survive without Bruce, honestly.

Blog Post: March 13, 2008 8:30 a.m.

Welcome to Hell

Yesterday Torran lost birth weight, as any baby would. Now he's gone from a not so bad looking preemie to the scary NICU skeleton preemie. More than once I caught myself wondering if he was dead. Seeing his heart beating where his ribs and belly meet and looking at the electronic display puts that worry to rest.

He's holding steady, with a few downs and some ups that we cling to fiercely. They're giving him 1mL of breast milk every four hours now and he's tolerating it well. No poops yet, but peeing OK. He's also off the nitric oxide completely, but still having small amounts of oxygen via the tube in his nose (which goes into his lungs). He also requires the machine to help him breathe because his breathing cannot keep his body balanced metabolically. As a result, he's had some issues with his blood gases and acid-base balances. The team keeps a close eye on it and makes corrections ASAP.

He was put under special lights to correct his increasing jaundice, hence the fuzzy looking goggles that cover his entire face. We call it Shake and Bake because the oscillating ventilator makes his body vibrate. I barely got to see his face yesterday. That was heart breaking. During morning care he opened his gorgeous eyes, giving us a little stare.

I have legs that are so full of fluid that they look like tree trunks and are very uncomfortable. 15 cm circumference! Even though I'm crying a lot, the fluid is not moving out of my legs because I spend most of my day upright on a stool. I feel like a disabled person in that I'm not able to move about without getting winded. I still get pelvic pains. It slows me right down.

The rest areas for parents at the hospital are appallingly small and provide little comfort.

At least my boobs provide Torran with good levels of food at the moment... not that he can eat it all.

We are humbled by all of the support we are given. But damn, do we need it!

CHAPTER 8

Blog Post: March 14, 2008 8:30 a.m.

Your Newborn Son has Bleeds in His Brain

Words that strike terror into our hearts.

Words which bring burning tears to already distraught eyes.

Words I hate.

Torran has bleeds in the middle of his brain in areas called the ventricles. It's a risk of premature birth. The bleeds are graded by severity from Grade 1 to Grade 4. 1 and 2 are most common, but pose the least risk factors and permanent problems. 3 and 4 are less common, and pose higher risks and permanent problems.

Torran has Grade 3 bleeds into both sides of his brain.

Today he'll have another ultrasound to determine whether or not the bleeding continued.

When they told us about his drop in hemoglobin, the bulging of his fontanelles, and of the high level of retained carbon dioxide in his blood, I suspected this might be the message we would receive. He had a blood transfusion which brought his hemoglobin level up correcting the anemia from the blood loss. It doesn't stop the bleeding.

I wasn't ready for it to be that grave. 24 hours after receiving the news, it still reduces me to a quivering mass.

I'm afraid of today's scan. We probably won't get it until Monday because the radiologist has to do his/her report and confer with the neonatologist.

Yesterday, Torran had a distended and taut belly. Day four after birth and he hadn't pooped yet. After the nurse introduced a tiny amount of suppository into his rectum with a small syringe, he finally pooped some of his meconium, a newborn's first poop. I got to do "mummy" stuff and change one of them. Yay!!

They pulled undigested breast milk out of his stomach. It raised a concern because it shouldn't have been there. They stopped that feed. At his next scheduled feeding time, he had what looked like bowel content in his stomach. Also something that's not supposed to be there. So his bowels have been given another rest from the feeds for now. Hopefully it's an issue of constipation and not a condition called necrotizing enterocolitis (NEC), also a risk of prematurity. Floored by the news of his brain bleed, I can't even contemplate the implications of NEC.

Through all of the incredible swings of emotion (and hell) we spent mummy and daddy time with our little man as we read him a book about a spider who plays golf (one of daddy's hobbies). Today we'll be reading a book about a mole who gets poop on his head, one of Bruce's childhood favourites, to encourage him to move his bowels. Pooping also helps treat his jaundice because it removes the bilirubin via the stool.

There's still so much more going on than I have conveyed here. It's all so overwhelming that I'm surprised we haven't had a breakdown.

CHAPTER 9

MARCH 14, 2008

Beep! Beep! Beep! Beep!

I stop reciting *Foursome the Spider* and glance up at the bedside monitor. The oxygen levels hold steady, despite the alarm raised by Torran's ventilator. His tiny splayed arms jerk towards his midline and his knees spasm upwards.

It's 4:45 p.m. He's having a break from the phototherapy for his jaundice and I'm able to see his face again. Having lost the excess fluid from birth, his features are chiseled and gaunt. Torran looks like a skeleton with a pulse beating against his chest. *His tiny heart.* He reminds me of an old man, particularly when he grimaces. His forehead wrinkles impart a wisdom he achieved before he was born. I call him my wee man, not my baby.

He squeezes his eyes shut as his limb movements continue. I cannot discern the source of his discomfort. There are so many possibilities, I draw a blank. I want to reach in and stroke his forehead smooth. My hand pauses at the door to his incubator. I can't touch him until I use the alcohol rinse. Acting contrary to my instincts kills me.

He stops moving and the warnings subside. His expression eases. A few lines remain on his forehead, an inviting pathway for my finger.

Instead of touching him, I brush a tear away from my eye. *You've had enough of this story for today.* I close the book.

Interestingly, *The Little Mole Who Knew it was None of His Business* didn't generate the same reaction. He must like the book as much as his Daddy. It didn't fix the problem with his belly, though. Torran's exposed abdomen remains shiny and tight, the top layers of skin peeling. He's backed up more than the 401 at rush hour during a winter storm.

Ignoring the growing ache in my legs, I ease myself out of one of the few visitors' chairs in the unit. Only a handful of parents spend the entire day here. Before I bring the receiving blanket down on my side of the incubator, I look through at Bruce on the other side.

He sits hunched over on a padded stool. A hand on one knee and an elbow on the other, he peers into the dim plastic box. There are more creases at the corners of his sunken eyes than last week. Small sweat patches creep out from under his arms.

We've been waiting all day for answers.

A sharp twinge in my breast reminds me that I last expressed milk three hours ago. *Must keep to that milking schedule.* Sealing out the light with the makeshift incubator cover, I move to Bruce's side.

"I should probably go pump." He gives me a goofy grin and I return it with a playful swat. "If the doctor comes..."

"I know where to find you," he turns away stretching. Darkness returns to his face as he turns back to his vigil.

Yesterday I pointedly told Dr. Salawu, a senior doctor, that I want the newest ultrasound result today, not after Monday's educational clinical rounds. The downfall of teaching hospitals is the delay of information to patients and families. The medical staff discusses and learns from the information before distributing it to parents and patients.

If I hid my profession in the pre-natal unit, I wear it as both shield and weapon in the NICU. Dr. Salawu agreed to give us the outcome before the end of the day.

I check the clock above Torran's spot. 4:50 p.m.

The constant electronic triggers and alarms don't faze me now. Many babies have mechanical Nannies waiting for that moment when oxygenation dips too low. Their mindful noises constantly fill the background. Nurses acclimate to the alerts, knowing which ones are too long or too frequent. If I didn't have similar firsthand experience, I'd be crying out for medical assistance every few minutes.

Beep! Beep! Beep! Beep!

This ventilator alarm of Torran's is the fifteenth for the day, often related to his movement. The doctors thought he might be off the breathing machine today. Torran had other plans. The day has been uneventful.

Neither Bruce nor I feel victorious in that.

Bruce sees the team arrive as I move to collect my rental pump from under the incubator. He puts his hand on my arm to stop me. Three people in white lab coats, Dr. Salawu and two others, and Torran's nurse Melissa arrive. Melissa took care of Torran when he arrived from the resuscitation room.

My hands feel cold. *It's time.* I grit my teeth and greet the entourage.

"Mr. and Mrs. Donaldson, thank you for waiting. We'd like to speak with you about the results." Dr. Salawu has a slight lisp in her voice, but it doesn't detract from its calm authority.

Not good. Not good.

I feel that pinching around my eyes which usually comes before the tears. As they lead us to a private room, I grope for tissues in my pocket, finding none.

The room is familiar. I attended a training class here years ago. Beige walls devoid of decoration envelop a small conference table. A whiteboard smeared with rubbed out words faces the doorway. Random supplies perch awkwardly in every corner. I squeeze past empty chairs and sit down. Last into the enclosure, Melissa seals us in.

This will not be fun.

Dr. Salawu blocks the view through interior window from the head of the table. She recaps what we already know about

Torran. I look at the table top, hiding my impatience. Her review ensures that we understand the forthcoming information. *If Bruce was a medical person, we could skip this torture.*

"Torran's first ultrasound result showed a Grade 3 bleed in both sides of his head, as you know."

The discomfort in my breasts increases. Under the desk, I squeeze Bruce's hand.

"I'm sorry to tell you that the bleeding increased," she says. "It's worse on the right. On that side, the blood invaded Torran's brain. Ultrasounds can't detail the full extent of the bleeding, because it scans the surface. I can tell you that the damage is in an area of his brain related to motor activity, and it will affect his left side. Beyond on that, I can't specify what part of the left side of his body will be affected or to what extent. It's likely he'll have cerebral palsy, a disorder that affects how muscles move. Or, he could be paralysed."

Melissa reaches across the table handing me a box of tissues. Tears smother my cheeks. Dr. Salawu pauses, hands in front of her. I sense there is more to come. Bruce, hand free from my grip, presses on his temple.

"So you can't tell us whether or not he'll be able to walk or move his arms? Or his leg?" His voice is the biggest thing in the room.

"No, I'm sorry I can't," she shakes her head and closes her mouth. She opens it again, takes a breath and stops. "There is another complication. The side with the Grade 3 bleed isn't damaging brain tissue right now but it could continue to bleed into the brain as well.

"In either case, this kind of bleeding often leads to increased pressure on the brain and other developmental problems because of the blood clots that form. Torran could develop hydrocephalus: fluid that is supposed to drain out of the brain becomes blocked and accumulates. Often, that needs surgical correction." She continues with her explanation but the words are a blur.

I try to blow my nose without disrupting her. This isn't the outcome I want. Melissa takes a tissue from another box, discretely dabbing at her eyes. The other doctors witness in silence. Dr. Salawu inhales and exhales slowly before she continues.

"Torran is on a machine that does his breathing for him. You don't have to make a decision now, but I have to tell you that this is the only kind of situation that creates the opportunity to remove that life support."

And let him die.

"If later on you change your mind about Torran's future and he is breathing without the ventilator, there's nothing we will do to change that."

This is not an eventuality Bruce and I discussed. The subdued beeps on the other side of the glass seem farther away as the room drifts away from me an ocean of mute tears.

Bruce looks to me, but I can't make eye contact with him. I'm not ready. What if our answers are different? Four pairs of eyes now look at me with sympathy; one with worry. I feel pressured to respond. Instead, I stall.

"Is there any... Does he react like you would expect a baby born like him to react? Like, with his reflexes?"

"I would say, yes, although he is very fragile."

"But he's not, you know, flat or limp or anything like that?" The correct terminology eludes me. I'm sure I sound less than intellectual.

"No, no. We don't see any of that right now. But I don't know what is going to happen to him. It could be a good progression, or things might go very poorly."

"Well, I know what..." the words stick to the roof of my mouth. How can I walk away without answering? How can I give an answer without talking to Bruce? We were so focused on Torran's breathing at birth, that we never discussed long term complications other than his lungs.

I stop myself from saying more and bury my eyes in the last tissue. Finally, I turn to Bruce, my lower lip curling down. "I don't think I'm ready to remove it yet." I don't dare ask him his opinion. *Will this divide us?*

"No," he says, reaching for me. He looks to Dr. Salawu. "No. We can't take out the tube yet. There's no discussion needed. It's too early."

Blog Post: March 14, 2008 10:28 p.m.

Do you want to remove your son's life support?

You are told that there is no right or wrong answer.

You are encouraged to take your time to decide.

You are reassured that the process has to reflect your family needs and capabilities.

You are not told how to stop the anticipation of your child's death or disability.

You are not protected from the grief that tears your heart out of your chest.

You are not able to look into the future to direct your path.

Torran, Bruce and I shared our worst moment

today. The repeated ultrasound showed that Torran's bleed increased on one side of his head to a Grade 4. This means that the blood leaked from the ventricle into the surrounding brain tissue and killed it.

The area involved is responsible for movement. Torran faces a high probability of being permanently paralyzed on one side of his body, arm and/or leg.

The other side of his brain may continue to bleed further, also making it a Grade 4. At present, it remains Grade 3, but the ventricle into which the blood is located is bulging slightly. He could develop hydrocephalus and require a shunt to correct the increased fluid in his head.

We received the information at 5:00 p.m. after enjoying Torran's first relatively stable day. We were told that there is a window of opportunity within which we could withdraw Torran's life support if we so chose.

We could remove the little tube that goes through his nose into his lungs and provides him with most of his breathing. Torran's not strong enough to breathe without this technology.

Essentially, he will die without it.

Seven weeks ago, we were told that it would be unlikely that he would be able to breathe at all. Termination of my pregnancy seemed like the only option that we had to prevent the pain of losing a child at birth.

At 34 minutes past midnight on the night of his birth, our little man breathed on his own for a miraculous four minutes before his body revealed that he needed the assistance from the medical team by being intubated (the tube in his nose).

Although he continues to need mechanical ventilation and adjustments to his blood chemistry, he is functioning as well as could be hoped. After resting his bowels for a night, the team doesn't think that he has necrotizing enterocolitis. He finally had another couple of meconium poops, but remains a little jaundiced. However, he's only required one of the three lights for phototherapy. His blood sugars are stabilizing, as is his sodium level.

And when he opens his eyes and looks at us, it is the most beautiful sight we have ever seen.

We informed the team of our decision.

This is the worst thing that has ever happened to us.

Torran is the best thing that has ever happened to us.

We chose the unknown path, flooded with our tears, and refused to pull out the tube.

CHAPTER 10

MARCH 15, 2008

A dim, narrow hallway leads to a small antechamber with a stainless steel trough. Coats and a stack of lock boxes crowd the space. Bruce and I stand at the sink scrubbing our hands like surgeons preparing for an operation.

Parents and visitors must have approval to enter the NICU. I pause before I pick up the phone that's connected to the nursing station.

"Let's just have a calm day today, OK?" The darkness under Bruce's eyes makes him look like a panda. The grooves in his face from his jovial spirit sit deeper today in quiet contemplation.

Someone answers the phone, but refuses us entry. I hang up and Bruce walks forward, assuming that we have permission. I place a hand on his chest.

"We can't go in. They're doing a lumbar puncture." I explain the need for sterility, as they're inserting a needing into Torran's spine. However, I can't figure out why the procedure is necessary.

Lumbar punctures diagnose infections of the spinal cord and brain. Torran hasn't had a fever or symptoms of infection.

Twenty minutes later, an unfamiliar doctor meets with us in the parent lounge. He stands in the doorway. From my seat on the couch he seems much larger than his five foot-something height. After his soft and brief handshake, his hands retire to the safety of the pockets in his white lab coat.

"Your son developed a fever overnight. We suspect he has an infection. We tried to call you at home to obtain permission for the lumbar puncture but there was no answer." My brain chews on the details.

I called during the night when I last pumped. It's part of my nightly routine. That was about 2:30 a.m. The nurse didn't report any problems. As always, Torran was "fine." *I hate that word.*

Bruce shakes his head. "We'd already left the house so we could be here for morning rounds. Neither of us turned our phones on."

"We have to assess all potential sources for infections. We sampled you son's blood already. Premature babies are at risk for meningitis, a brain infection. The lumbar puncture removes some of the fluid that bathes the brain and spinal cord out of the body, which we then test for bacteria. It's been tough though, because we're having problems getting the proper sample.

"We insert a needle between the bones of the spine and tap into the fluid between the linings of the spinal cord," the doctor says. Bruce winces. The doctor hastily completes his update and returns to the baby that won't cooperate.

I don't want to imagine my fragile infant held in a fetal position that stretches out the lower part of his spine for the needle access. If they can't get the needle into his back properly, they'll keep at it repeatedly.

The thought of my child enduring that torture without me makes me find enough strength to stand up. In three steps I cross the room and look out the window. There is nowhere to go.

Sunshine cannot get into the window, strangled by the buildings that surround us to the outside world. Under that wide blue sky some mother holds her baby, her body rocking like a pulse. I wrap my arms around the empty space on my chest.

An hour passes during which I ignore Bruce's attempts at keeping me calm.

"If they're doing a lumbar puncture means that he's really sick."

"You don't know that, Lesley. The doctor didn't say that."

"Are you kidding me? You do know what I do for a living don't you?" We dance the Who's Right Tango until I tire of talking to him.

Impatiently, I pick up phone in the parent lounge. *I want in.* The same cheery voice as before answers the phone. I select incitant words.

"I want to see my son before he dies." Bruce gives me a sharp look, sucking air in through his teeth.

My plan worked.

"Oh it's nothing like that," she says. "You can come see him now."

The tiny cotton cap and flannel blanket on Torran nearly remove him from sight. He's not supposed to need that in this heated box. Before we can settle in to see him properly, a young Asian doctor asks to speak to us privately.

Shit. Not that room again.

My eyes find new salty reserves. I thought I could be brave today. She leads us away, captives of impending news.

Same room. Same parents. Different doctors. Different news.

This is an extended nightmarish déjà vu from yesterday. The blind, open today, allows strips of over-bright light into the room. Dr. Yeung is as youthful as yesterday's counterpart, with silent Dopplegangers in-training. Only the senior doctor on staff delivers really bad news, it seems. Today's nurse sits at the table.

I felt compelled to be in the NICU earlier. Now, my brain screams "get out" like the voyeur of a horror film. A muted alarms sounds and I wonder if it's Torran's.

Dr. Yeung tells us that Torran has sepsis. More to Bruce than to me, she explains that they suspect infection. Overnight his blood pressure dropped and he developed a fever.

Why didn't they call us when they knew something was wrong?

The team took specimens from every possible source seeking

a cause. Three attempts at a lumbar puncture failed. I look away from her at this, banning the thought of what Torran underwent from my brain.

"We're prophylactically treating him with antibiotics to be on the safe side. If we need to, we can adjust the medication when the results come back."

Nurse Mom kicks into high alert mode, leaving her husband behind as an afterthought. "What about his pressure?"

The doctor answers me directly. "He's being treated with dopamine and fluid boluses right now. We can add on norepinephrine as a second inotrope if there's little improvement. And he'll probably need another blood transfusion."

I don't want to look in her eyes. Her eyes will tell the truth. I only want the lie, when I ask *that* question.

Is that my life circling the drain too?

My eyes stay trained on hers. "If you use both inotropes and it doesn't work, what then?"

She pauses. "I'm afraid that's all we can do."

There are no muscles left in my body. My hands catch my face as I slump over into a pool of mucous and tears.

Bruce reaches for me. He places his hand on my arm because I won't emerge from the barrier I created.

"I don't understand," he says to the doctors. "What does that mean?"

"If his heart stops, they can't get it back," the loud staccato of my voice throws the doctor off of her structured response. "He'll die."

Blinking, he looks back at the doctor. I succumb to angry sobs.

The doctor's tone remains level, "In sepsis, the fluid leaks out into the surrounding tissues. That's why your son's blood pressure dropped. If we can't fix it, his heart can't pump fluid that isn't there, not even with CPR."

Bruce must be reacting in some way. I don't know. I can't bring myself to look at him, even after I clear the evidence of my heartbreak off my face.

Nothing exists in the world at this moment except for the image I have of a son I might never know. Instead of a boy wiggling impatiently during a grade school performance, I see the skeleton with a heartbeat in a plastic box.

"There is another matter to consider," Dr. Yeung states. I lift my head, an ostrich looking for danger. Across from us the younger female physician remains taciturn and avoids eye contact. She presses the tips of her thumbs on her folded hands.

"With such a low pressure, there is a risk of hypoxemia to the brain," Dr. Yeung looks at Bruce, "a lack of oxygen." I reach for him grasping the same hand that gave me strength when I brought our child into the world.

"He has the damage in his brain from birth, as you know. This lack of oxygen may contribute further damage but I wouldn't be able to say to what extent. The low blood pressure poses a significant risk to his development even if he responds to the medication. I know you were asked this question yesterday, and I'm very sorry that I'm asking you again today.

"Would you like to remove Torran's life support?"

My vocal cords died when I heard that Torran's heart cannot be resuscitated. I'm sure of it. I shake my head without looking to Bruce for confirmation. Thankfully, he voices the same opinion.

"You don't have to make a decision right now, of course. The option remains so long as your son is on a ventilator," she stresses. More words of condolence fall from her lips, but only one phrase catches my attention.

"If you would like, you can hold him."

"Seriously?" The offer yanks my voice out of perdition.

"Studies show that a Kangaroo hold help babies regulate

temperature and improves their breathing status," she answers smiling.

Yes! Yes! I will heal him with the power of my warmth. The thought of cradling my son for the first time pushes the pain from my eyes.

At his incubator, we draw up chairs waiting to hold the most precious thing in our lives. My head battles my emotions for serenity.

The dark-haired nurse from the room of doom introduces herself as Melissa. "Mom and Dad," her carefully chosen words come out slowly, "I know that the doctor said you could hold Torran. But I advise against it. His IV is in the only vein I was able to access. I put it in his foot. He's peripherally shut down. If that site goes we would lose everything that we've done to save him."

I know those words. I've said them.

My heart aches so much, but I don't argue. I won't risk Torran's life so I can hold him.

Visitors arrive for the other babies in the unit. Melissa places a screen around us preventing the looky-loos upon our near-death child. She lifts the side panel of the box out of the way and turns up the incubator's radiant heat. The bottom slides out like a tray, bringing a bundled Torran two inches closer to us.

Beneath the hat and blankets, his skin is a sickly grey hue; jaundice yellow his only colour. Tiny eyelashes dot flat eyelids. Torran sluggishly opens his eyes for mere seconds before they close again. He barely moves, this child who previously wriggled in his own party.

I beg my child in a hushed voice, "Please come home. I promise you a life of love and caring, no matter what. Daddy and I love you so much. Just please, please get better and come home."

Bruce repetitively mutters, "I'm so sorry."

We have no way of knowing whether or not Torran hears us over the noise of his ventilator. *I didn't know it was so loud.* The plastic wall muffled the suppressed the volume of the machine.

Somewhere beneath the blankets, his little foot sprouts the intravenous line fed by the pump on the pole beside Torran's bed. We sit uselessly between the two tethers that keep our son alive.

An alarm signals from the monitor over our heads. A blue electronic line measuring oxygen and flashing red zero shouts for attention.

"Oh God, not now!" I look to the breathing corpse that is my son. *I'm not ready for you to leave me.* Bruce squeezes my thigh.

Melissa's reaction is the opposite of my panic. I wasn't aware that she was behind me.

"No no," she says softly, her gentle hand on my shoulder, "it's just a loose probe. He's fine." We give up our front row seats letting her take care of the attachments. The green telemetry line beats steadily at 170 beats per minute. Of course, she's right. He's fine: Torran is alive.

I still hate that word.

We enter the cafeteria, neither of us hungry. We'll be staying at the hospital tonight in the "Care By Parent" room and must make plans. In that converted hospital room with a queen sized bed parents either wait for their child to die, or get a test run at rooming in with baby before the infant goes home. We avoid discussing whether or not it will be the last time we'll be with our son.

I find the most remote corner of the deserted cafeteria and turn my back upon its empty chairs. My hands shake as I dial the number to my mother.

Bruce already called his parents in Scotland. They are supposed to arrive in June, when Torran should have been born.

We asked them to stay put for the moment. They're waiting to hear from us whether or not they need to change their flight.

My mother answers her phone and listens without interruption as I recount the morning's events, including the risk of Torran's death.

"Oh honey. Oh honey." There is nothing else she can say.

"Am I keeping him alive because I want to have my baby boy at home? Is it fair to put him through this?"

I cry into the phone, unsuccessfully curling my large frame into the tiniest ball on the uncomfortable chair. Bruce returns from the cashier and hands me thin serviettes for the tears dominating my face. They shred the delicate material.

"My little boy is so sick. I don't know how much he is suffering." The void of the room behind me feels oppressive. "I don't know what he wants me to do."

For the first time, I doubt myself. I feel like I can't make a competent decision. Or, if I do, I'm completely selfish and not taking Bruce's feelings or Torran's future into consideration.

I know Bruce and I started this journey together, and so far, we've been on the same path. But what if I'm wrong? What if he doesn't want a son with life of unknown disability? A split decision between us now could have profound effects on our marriage.

And what of the fragile wee man fighting death upstairs? I don't know what life we'll be denying him.

Will he ever forgive me if I make him live?

Blog Post: March 15, 2008 10:39 p.m.

Deathwatch

We arrived today to find out our little man
has a suspected infection.

He's a critically ill little boy.

I cannot write. I am so numb.

CHAPTER 11

MARCH 18, 2008

I'm holding Torran on my chest, the classic pose of a mother asleep with her baby. Only he's the wrong way around. He should be in line with my body, not across. Why is he so heavy?

Abrupt daylight bleaches my dream to oblivion. Torran's weight remains palpable. I turn to my side. My breast slams into its twin.

Squinting at the bedside clock, I realize I missed my overnight pumping. My breasts are engorged bowling balls. I'm supposed to pump every three hours as if I were feeding a newborn. I can push it to five without too much discomfort, but this is ridiculous!

My laughter uplifts me for the first time since Torran's brain bleeds were diagnosed. I wake Bruce and give him an eye full of the mammoth boobs. His incredulous guffaw returns mirth to the eyes recently possessed by pain.

Torran didn't die on the weekend, although all the staff expected it. Melissa offered to have Torran blessed by the on-call Minister. Bruce refused, his sarcasm burning her ears. I'm not a practicing Roman Catholic any more, but I didn't want a minister of any faith to bless Torran. It felt like saying goodbye.

We spent the second day of our vigil reading to him, telling him that we love him, and asking him not to give up on himself. Watching his inert body tore me apart as I considered his immediate future. Bruce rarely left Torran's side.

I asked Torran to tell me what he wanted us to do - how did he want us to decide? He only grimaced.

We were supposed to be at the hospital again last night.

83

Torran had episodes of bradycardia. A trainee doctor from Saturday's baleful meeting didn't know the cause. She barely looked us in the eye all weekend.

In the afternoon, plans changed. The team asked us to let another couple stay in the Care By Parent room. We were ecstatic. It meant that Torran was no longer the sickest child in the NICU. Then I felt guilty. *I'm sorry that it's your child's turn.*

To try and feel better, I commemorated Torran's first week of life sharing baked goods with hospital staff. The trainee female doctor looked me in the eye when she received the one week birthday cupcake.

Torran's not as grey as he was when he was septic, but I wouldn't say he has a healthy colour either. The jaundice returned when his bowels stopped again. Neither of us likes the taut dome that is Torran's abdomen. Despite the nurses' attempts, the meconium didn't come out completely. Bruce won't discuss the risk of bowel perforation. It's too much for him to handle.

The intense tightness in my breasts eases as the suction of the breast pump starts. Bruce's tender kisses linger on my forehead. Our interactions with each other are back to normal.

At one point during our emotionally complex weekend in the Care By Parent Room, I feared that we faced an impasse in our marriage. I sat propped against pillows, my swollen legs unable to bear my weight any longer. He sat hunched at the side of the bed beyond my reach.

My heart stood alone at the divide.

I swore I would take Torran home under any circumstance. Bruce said he couldn't match my ability to care for a very high needs child. He loves Torran, but his fear of his unknown future cast deep doubts upon his parenting capabilities.

Torran lay motionless in the box.

We had no idea what to do, or how we could cope. Finally, we agreed that Torran, not the doctors, will tell us what degree of brain damage he has, even though the process may take months.

Our hearts united across the chasm.

Paradoxically, we still wonder how much his tiny body can take and at what point it will be too much either for him or for us.

There is no easy answer.

At Mt. Sinai there are an average of 34 babies in the Level Three NICU and 16 in the Level Two Special Care Nursery. Of these children, each has family and friends who journey with them through their daily struggles.

Every NICU family has heart stopping moments. A parent whose child faces these incredible hurdles holds their breath, bargains with unseen forces, and hopes for the most positive outcome. Parents seek miracles each moment of each day, regardless of the families' religion, or lack thereof.

To our relief, the amoeba of lab coats and clip boards had an abbreviated discussion about Torran today. Bruce and I feel grateful that parents are encouraged to participate in these brief dialogues each morning. We haven't missed one yet.

The wee man who kept everyone on tenterhooks before pulls at the thin feeding tube in his mouth. It's a sign he's starting to feel better.

I begged for my son's life. He gave us at least three more days.

I still avoid looking into my own eyes, afraid of the answers I would find there.

Would I have removed Torran's life support? *No.*

Would I have agreed to withholding CPR if the medications to support his heart had failed? It was the path my son's tiny body seemed to be taking. Then, yes, probably. *How could I choose that option?*

Seeing Torran's improvement helps lift the heavy fog in my head. His blood pressure holds steady. He's peeing well again. Although the bacterial cultures all came back negative, the doctors recommended that Torran completes a double antibiotic treatment.

"Now, Now. We'll have none of that little man," his nurse, Nancy, scolds Torran in a soft high pitched voice. The grey hair cropped past her chin veils her face as she reaches through the incubator door to stop her naughty patient.

We're on the hunt for primary nurses. They'll care for Torran throughout his hospitalization. Both nurses named Melissa declined our request. Yesterday's nurse had unquestionable clinical skill, but her personality was too dry for my over-ly-sensitive state of being. *This may take longer than we thought.*

Nancy has a no-nonsense manner about her, but she's not a brute. She speaks to Torran conversationally even though he won't respond. I like her immediately.

"Would you like to hold him, Mom?"

"I'm sorry, what?" There isn't a sound in the unit except her words.

"Usually we change the incubators every seven days, but Torran was sick at the time. I'd like to do it today. He has to come out for the transfer. If the RT agrees, you can hold him for the minute it takes me to prepare his new one." I don't need any encouragement.

Torran and I shared a twenty minute staring competition in the very early hours during the overnight deathwatch. Torran won hands down. His unending unfocused gaze melted my heart.

Holding him promises to trump that precious moment.

The petite RT agrees to manually ventilate Torran while I hold him. "You've got a good nurse in Nancy," she says. "This isn't a conventional practice."

Nancy parcels Torran in bulky blankets and places him in my arms. Wires and tubes dangle from the bundle like jelly fish tentacles. My eyes sting as I blink away tears. I won't mar the first time I hold my son with sadness.

I stand because there isn't any room for a chair between the dirty and clean incubators. All I feel are the blankets. I can barely tell he's there.

Torran's not opening his eyes. He screws his face up under the too bright lights. His head is so small I could cup it in my palm. The tapes mashed against his nose draw his lip upwards uncomfortably, not letting his mouth close. I can't rock him to soothe him. Each motion tugs on the tube that distorts his face. Beside me the RT squeezes a black plastic bulb attached to the tube in Torran's nose. She is his lungs.

Bruce takes pictures. The nurses know me as the mother who photographs everything, including the day he almost died. We've promised each other that no one will ever see those heartbreaking pictures until Torran's old enough to tell us otherwise.

When my mother came to see him on Sunday, she broke down crying in the hallway saying "he's so small." In my arms, Torran is even more diminutive and fragile. *What if I drop him?*

As much as I crane my neck towards Torran I'm not able to kiss him. Bruce strokes the tiny patch of Sharpai pup skin that is his forehead. If Torran grows to his father's height, he's going to need all those folds.

Sixty seconds later, it's all over. Parts of my body ache from the strain; others from the emotional longing. I held my baby eight days after he was born.

On the drive home, my cheeks cramp from smiling as I share the news on my cell. The single minute instantaneously turned me into a cuddle junkie. *I want my next fix.*

For the first time since Friday, I looked at myself in the mirror and wasn't afraid of what I saw.

CHAPTER 12

MARCH 25, 2008

Mt. Sinai's large Level 3 NICU is roughly rectangular. Plastic boxes housing infants surround the room, and line the central wall in the middle. The pathway through the care spaces reminds me of a casino. You're trapped inside with unpredictable chances of winning but superstition tells you that if you leave, you'll lose.

On the walls, teddy bears in frilly clothes cavort on green hills, blissfully unaware of the sickly children below, unlike me - the living witness who remembers.

There is an empty incubator a few beds away from us. It held a baby who was born too early whilst the twin remained *in utero*. The baby's family decided upon comfort measures for the problems wrought upon their prematurely born child. Or, they didn't have a choice. I don't know the details.

The baby died on Friday. The white dividing screen around the bed is gone.

I find myself staring at the space instead of the grinning fur balls. How will that mother grieve with the twin still inside her? Will she and her partner always see a reminder of their other child in the face of the survivor? I don't know which is the lesser evil. It's something I can't imagine.

There are unsettling vibes around Torran. One baby's oxygen frequently swings from 60 to 100%. Another's heart rate drops to seventy, half of what it should be. The baby doesn't respond to the nurses' interventions easily.

I cleanse my hands and place my finger in Torran's sleepy grip. His fingers curl reflexively. The recent invasive procedures drained his energy. He has few wakeful moments.

"Daddy and I love you very much, Wee Man. You keep fighting your big fight with your tiny body. I am *so* proud of you." I can't repeat the words enough.

Torran exists between a fetal and an infant state. We're told he can hear us. I assume that's true if his ear bones developed properly and his brain has sound wiring. There's certainly no way he comprehends language yet.

Babies have an acute sense of smell. We probably reek of hand rinse. He may think his parents are alcoholics.

I don't know that he's able to focus on my face properly because I'm always behind the plastic wall of the incubator, several inches away.

All I can do is hope that somehow he knows his parents are here, and that he's loved. It's so unfair that this innocent child will spend the first months of his life enduring harshness. I have to put him through it if he is to have a chance of survival, even though it hurts me to do so.

Everyone keeps telling us that our family is strong and inspiring. Then why do I feel like I'm losing the will to fight?

An aura of gloom possesses me. I can't shake it, even though the weather outside is brilliant. Not a day passes without tears.

I'm not a person who indulges in self-pity. We don't know how to repay everyone's kindness, positivity and generosity. Feeling desolate seems like an offense to them, as if I'm rejecting their encouragement.

But, I can't run away from this. There is a reason why I'm here for so long every day. It's more than my internal drive to stay informed about Torran's medical progression. I'm his advocate and the attestant to his plight.

I can't be a "normal" mother no how much I yearn to hold Torran. Like the other families here, Bruce and I adapted to a new modality of family life for our emotional survival.

These clinicians and therapists know more about our babies'

functioning than we do. *It seems that way.* Well-trained, proficient strangers care for our children. *They don't kiss away the big boo-boos.*

On March 22ⁿᵈ, Torran needed a peripherally inserted central catheter. The PICC is a specialized intravenous that enters in his upper arm and ends near his heart. It's one of those painful interventions Torran must endure.

His stomach remains distended and he can't digest full volumes of milk. We celebrated when he cleared more of his meconium (*Who else celebrates poop but parents?*). There's no placental blood left in his stomach.

Torran's blood sugars and chemistry remain out of whack. He needed Transparenteral Nutrition, or TPN, in addition to the single millilitre of breast milk he gets every six hours.

The milky looking TPN is highly concentrated and damages veins. His umbilical vein is short and too old. Hence the need for a PICC line.

The first two insertion attempts occurred after I left the hospital. I found out when I called that evening. Since his septic episode, I call three times a day from home: before bed, after the overnight pump and before I depart for the hospital in the morning.

It killed me that I wasn't present to comfort him after the doctor's first stabs at it. Concentrated sugar on a soother is not a replacement for my arms. *If I could hold him in my arms.*

After four failed attempts, the doctors sent Torran across the street to Sick Kids Hospital. Rather, he went through the tunnel that connects the buildings. Using ultrasound to guide him, a Sick Kids radiologist inserted the PICC on his second try.

The cumulative interventions made Torran's hemoglobin levels drop nearly forty points. He needs another blood transfusion. We're hoping Bruce can directly donate.

I pull my hands out of the incubator and shut the door. I

study Torran's mechanical breathing as he lies on his IV-free belly. The peeling skin is as bad on his back as it was on his front. The humidity of the pretend uterus isn't enough for his friable skin. His body should be immersed in water right now.

Torran is 16 days old. The nurses try maintaining a fetal position, but he often wriggles out of the rolled blanket. When stretched out, he's 34 centimetres long. I rarely see him at that length.

Torran gained weight, but he still looks like a skeleton. He weighs 920 grams, the weight of one and half loaves of sliced bread. Our wedding rings fit up to his shoulder when we put them on him like bracelets.

Jen approaches us. "Hey Lesley, how's he liking the tummy?"

"No alarms yet."

Nancy became the first primary nurse. Torran's second, Jen, is a ringer for the blonde actress Cameron Diaz.

"Maybe it will help with all that gas in his belly." Jen's smile rivals that of her Hollywood counterpart. "Is Bruce here?"

"He's on the phone to the blood bank to make an appointment."

"Yeah," she says wrinkling her upper lip in apology, "I know yesterday they were saying he wasn't going to have the transfusion, but I guess the docs think it will be better for his recovery. Is Bruce donating?"

"Apparently, he's in the small percentage of fathers who are eligible," I easily fall into nursing parlance. "Bruce is excited. He thinks a directed donation is the only impactful thing he can do for Torran's recovery. He feels pretty useless."

Jen nods her head. "A lot of parents, and fathers in particular, feel that way. Bit of roller coaster, eh?"

Roller coaster. The NICU metaphor doesn't work for us. We love roller coasters; we hate what is happening to our baby.

Bruce describes being here as breaking every bone in your

body, and so far you only have two fingers healed. To me, it's winning a brand new sports car which arrives squashed down to a wrecker's cube. You have to ding it out bit by bit with a small hammer.

Bruce storms in, his face flaming red. I suspect we're about to experience another compaction to our sports car.

"They fucking won't let me donate!" Thankfully, the babies are too young to replicate Bruce's expletives and there aren't any other parents around.

"What? Why not?"

"I'm British, so I have mad cow disease." His rant attracts the attention of a couple of nurses.

"When I called to make the appointment, the intake person asked screening questions. One of them was whether or not I travelled in the United Kingdom between 1984 and 2001. I thought she was taking the piss because of my accent. I told her that I lived there. She said that because of the risk of Creutzfeldt-Jakob disease, I can't give blood to my own son!"

"Not even when I was there and ate British beef before and during my pregnancy? And we have every intention of taking our child there? That's ridiculous!" Creutzfeldt-Jakob disease is a fatal neurological communicable illness affecting one person in one million world-wide. Bruce doesn't answer my rhetorical questions.

He continues venting, swearing in nearly every sentence. His angry restlessness creates a stir. The charge nurse, a petite brunette who declined our entry into the Unit on the Ides of March, moves through the crowd.

If she tosses him out now, I'll lose my cool. Instead, she curiously asks him questions.

"You may not be a mad cow, but you look like a red bull," she offers, hiding her amusement behind her small hand.

The comment evokes subdued smirks in the faces around

him, including me. It's not that we're laughing at Bruce. He just looks so goofy with his straw-blonde hair topping off a cherry red face, a banana sundae in reverse.

It's going to be a long time before Bruce recovers from this rejection. The bears on the wall and the boy in the box continue in their tableaux, oblivious to the Scottish berserker beside them.

CHAPTER 13

MARCH 26, 2008

A month ago, a random doctor wished Bruce "Happy Birthday" after telling him his son might not live.

Today, Bruce holds his son for the first time.

He's sitting perched on the stool, shoulders tense and elbows held close. Bruce is barely breathing. Lisa, the RT who helped Torran with his first breaths, coaxes Bruce to relax.

"I'm afraid of dropping him," Bruce chuckles, looking to her. His voice suggests a calm composure despite the tension evident in his posture. *I'm so proud of you.*

"You're doing a great job, Dad," she says smiling. Bruce's hands span wider than the package he cradles, with IV lines, monitor wires and ventilator tubing protruding from both ends. *We're still not allowed to have a Kangaroo hold.*

Beside Lisa, the ventilator moves air in and out of Torran's lungs. The machine grants him the breath of life. His spirit gives him the fight to live.

Torran's nurse, a Filipino named Jenn, prepares a new incubator for him. We asked her to be Torran's last primary before I asked if Bruce could hold Torran during the incubator exchange. *Maybe she'll regret saying yes.*

Torran has had four stable days, with few changes to his daily medical interventions. He shows slow continuous recovery from the sepsis and in the progression of his overall health.

I snap a picture over Bruce's shoulder. Torran's eyes are narrow slits. He's buried in blankets showing only his face's flat colour.

After five minutes of the first Daddy cuddle, Jenn turns to me, tucks her long dark hair behind her ears, and delivers today's second surprise.

"Would you like a turn, Mom?"

MARCH 27, 2008

Bright lights glare in my eyes through the incubator's walls. They're hotter than I realize and I wonder if it will affect Torran.

"Look at him like you haven't seen him for a long while and you're really happy to see him," the television producer coaches me.

My 17 day old baby will appear in a commercial for the hospital. The camera operator filmed shots of the four pumps on Torran's IV pole and the machines surrounding his bed.

Obviously the producer doesn't know that I'm here every day, and has no idea what would make me truly happy. She should direct me to imagine that Torran's scans were erroneous and his brain is undamaged. Better yet, she could tell me that this is all a dream. When I wake up I'll be pregnant in my 29th week of gestation.

In my third trimester, I'd be gaining weight rapidly as my developed fetus' body increases in size. The maternity clothes that I purchased with my Christmas gift certificate will finally fit my ponderous belly. My skin will glow as my increased blood flow supports the life within me. In two more months, I'd walk with a waddle and bitterly complain about the tribulations of being pregnant. *If I'm ever pregnant again, I won't sweat the small stuff.*

The cameraman captures footage of my superficial happiness.

"Okay, great. We'll have you stay there and get some shots with the doctor." A sophisticated looking blonde woman in a business suit walks up to the incubator. She's not phased when the camera disrespectfully reveals every rib in Torran's chest. She tilts her head at me kindly. *She's not an actress.*

Bruce tells Jenn that we were chosen for the filming because he amused the nursing staff with his mad cow outburst. She raises her eyebrows at him.

"Then it's your fault that I'm appearing in this commercial," Jenn accuses him with a grin.

We're getting a reputation amongst the nurses. The Donaldsons are the parents who hang out all day making jokes with the staff. *When we aren't watching Torran struggle.*

We're the parents who won't let our kid die. After Torran's latest dramatic episode we asked the doctors to stop offering the removal of the ventilator. It's too stressful to sit in that suffocating room and receive information no parent should hear, much less have to think about whether or not we'll "pull the plug."

Bruce and I made our decision clear. Until Torran tells us otherwise, we don't want the alternative presented to us. Our answer remains unchanged.

It's clear that Torran sets his own schedule. He's earned the moniker of Murphy. If something is going to go wrong, our Murphy will find it.

We try buffering bad news and unfathomable events with humour. On Easter weekend, I attached construction paper bunny ears onto a hat my mother-in-law knitted for Torran and took a photo. That was the extent of our celebration. Torran was allowed to wear it long enough for a photograph. His hollowed appearance was a far cry from an Anne Geddes baby.

The woman in the suit dons a blue hospital gown as she feeds Torran one milliliter of breast milk. It's a mock precaution for television. If she wanted to look more medical, she should be wearing gloves and a yellow isolation gown...and the puffy blue cap.

For another shot, Bruce and I sit together on side of Torran's incubator, gazing at him "with adoration" as instructed.

We stifle a laugh under this scrutiny. I suppose that we're not the most romantic looking couple at the moment, because the producer makes us perform eight takes of sharing a kiss. By the end, it feels more tedious than tender.

We vacate our stools, my backside numb. The featured performer for the event records his portion of the commercial in front of Torran's incubator. Jenn tells us about the woman the suit.

"That's Dr. Kearney. She's one of the top docs." Jenn says. I haven't seen her before. Then again, she's probably very involved in the research and political side of the unit.

There are so many staff members involved in Torran's care that I'm rapidly losing track of who's who. I used to have a list of names, people to thank in a card when I return home, but I've lost the energy to maintain it.

The singer records his line several times, too. I guess Bruce and I aren't so bad at kissing as I thought.

Looking around the unit now, you'd never know it was an eventful day.

"Looks like it's just you and me this evening, Wee Man." Bruce went home earlier, needing sleep before his night shift.

Torran doesn't register my statement, as usual. Despite the hour long exposure to the blazing light of the camera, he seems the same. I almost halted filming process out of concern for his well-being. The lack of alarms indicates that he's coped well with his unusual day.

The wall clock reads 4:30 p.m. I'll stay for Torran's evening care and meet the evening nurse at shift change. When Torran was born, I committed myself to spending long days at his side. After all, if he was full term, I'd be home with him all day. *There's nothing for me at home.*

I look through the pictures from today's activities. At the

beginning of the camera's memory card, I pause at a picture of Torran in a kilt. Rather, he's wearing a kilt made for a beer can. It's too big around his waist. I could fit two of him in its circumference.

When I reach for the camera bag under the bed, I notice a piece of paper sticking out of Torran's medical binder. Unlike other hospital units, this unit keeps the patient's chart on the working desk next to the baby. Parents aren't prohibited from accessing the book.

I flip the cover open. There's a slot on the inside for "recent information" which the nurse integrates into his chart. The paper is Torran's latest ultrasound report. We weren't expecting the information until tomorrow. *But I have to read it now.*

Three words jump out at me.

Bilateral non-communicating hydrocephalus.

I read it twice, ensuring there's no mistake. The other details aren't as consequential. This is not the result I'm expecting. Torran had imaging of his brain last week. He didn't show any further damage from the brain bleeds diagnosed during his first week of life. I thought we weren't going to get any surprises in this follow-up scan.

There's a choking feeling in my throat. I bite my lip and keep my mouth closed as Jenn comes to the bedside, a container of frozen milk in hand. Soon it will be time for Torran's evening care.

"You OK?" she asks, soft brown eyes scanning me closely.

"The ultrasound result wasn't so good," I say, my voice shaking slightly. She nods. I look away from her, a silent request that she leave. She retreats to her other patient. I resist the pressure in my eyes until I can't keep the sadness at bay.

I control the tears for Torran's six o'clock care. This is as close to being a mother as I get. *It's hard to feel like a mother when you're staring at a box all day.*

Jenn checks Torran's stomach by pulling back on the syringe attached to feeding tube. It's empty. I draw up less than a teaspoon of defrosted milk and push it into the end of the feeding tube that remains taped to the wall of the incubator. The far end passes through his mouth into his stomach.

I measure his temperature under his arm. He wriggles. I remove the preemie diaper that engulfs his lower body and Torran's face screws up as if he's crying.

There's a scale underneath him and I lift Torran within the incubator while Jenn zeros it. He would be close enough to kiss if it weren't for the plastic roof.

Another nurse interrupts the quiet rhythm of our routine actions. Jenn's other patient has been very ill today. The baby needs her intervention. I assure her that I can finish alone.

I sit with both hands through the holes in the incubator, cupping Torran's head and scrawny legs as he calms from his handling. Without the distraction of Torran's evening care, my thoughts race through my head. The tears stream down my face unbidden. *Where is the camera now?*

Hydrocephalus is a risk of the bleeds in Torran's head. Blood in his brain clotted and now blocks the normal drainage of fluid. We knew this could happen. *I prayed that it wouldn't.*

I feel hopeless. I can't stop asking myself "Why him? What did he do to deserve this?"

Did we make a mistake?

Torran returns to his coma-like state. The ventilator makes him breath and the heart monitor shows his heart beats.

Raindrops stain my lap faster than I can blot them.

"I'm so sorry, Wee Man. Mummy can't stay here tonight. I'm so sorry."

Without facing anyone on my way out, I leave the hospital. I'd run if my legs weren't so swollen.

Sitting beside the window on the rush-hour subway means

I'm staring at myself in the reflection if I avoid the passenger's stares. *I don't want to look there either.* There's mucous bubbling at my nostrils because I don't have tissues in my pocket. Sniffling keeps it at bay. I wipe my eyes on the upturned collar of my jacket as I bury myself deep in its folds.

Self Pity Me is having a party tonight. I hate her. I hate feeling this way. I hate what is happening to my son.

Guilt smacks me in the face.

How dare I feel bad that my child might need brain surgery? Another woman might lose her newborn tonight. At least my son has a chance to live.

Pessimist Me and the Defiant Optimist Me wrestle for domination over my emotions. If I make eye contact with rubberneckers, they hastily turn away. No one offers me a tissue.

Bruce picks me up at the end of the line. I sputter the details of the report through the mucous and tears as he drives home. Before I remove my coat, I collapse into the protection of his arms. Sobbing replaces my words.

"Just wait until tomorrow. Let's see what they say tomorrow," he repeats quietly, refusing to let me fall.

CHAPTER 14

MARCH 30, 2008

I'm crammed in the elevator waiting for the doors to open. The passengers' clothes emit a musty smell as the stowaway snow melts, especially from the man in a wool coat.

My ambitious plan to regain my health by walking up the seven flights of steps to the NICU is a distant memory. At first I blamed my uncomfortably swollen legs. The truth is, I've given up. I can't battle my weight and prevent depression at the same time.

The doors open and I squeeze into the elevator foyer. Before my delivery, I had at least a tenuous pulse on the outside world. Now, anything other than events within the hospital seems foreign and strange. *Is this what detachment feels like?*

Yesterday, I walked into a tour group of third trimester women on a hospital orientation tour. I nearly had a panic attack trying to get past them without looking at their bellies. My fragile composure couldn't bear another incident like that.

Peeking around the corner before I step out, I let out my breath. My steps take me past the entrance to the birthing suites and into the narrow NICU hallway.

It's the last day of my least favourite month. I can't remember the last time March brought me pleasure. *Tomorrow will be different.*

"Hello, Wee Man. Mummy's here," I greet Torran through the hole in his incubator. He's not moving much. We're on the watch for infection again because of irregularities in his blood. *I'm not ready for that to happen.*

"Guess what? I brought an incubator cover for your friend Nicholas like the one Mummy's friend made for you." Nicholas is Torran's NICU buddy. The boys were born within a week of each other, and of a similar gestation. We often chat with his parents. I wave to his mother at the end of the row. "I'll be back, sweetheart." My hands aren't warm enough for touching him anyways.

I want to hear Nicholas' latest update. His PICC line moved into his chest last week and the infusing IV fluid collapsed his lung. Maria, his mother, was his early warning system. He's shown enough recovery to move off the ventilator to the next breathing modality.

"So, how did things go with the doctor yesterday?" Maria has as much interest in Torran as I do in her son. I told her about discovering the hydrocephalus diagnosis accidentally. We both read through our son's charts regularly. Her husband calls it a dicey habit.

"Actually, it's a good thing that I found the ultrasound report a day early. This time when we met the new doctor, Dr. Ling, in that horrible room, we held our composure because we knew what was coming." Before the meeting, Bruce researched the diagnosis. He felt like he was able to ask better questions.

"They told us that Torran has an advantage over an older child. As his brain swells from the accumulating fluid, it pushes the skull plates apart. He'll have less pressure on his brain than if his bones were fused together, like when he grows."

"So it could do less damage?"

"That's the idea, although you know what it's like here." I roll my eyes.

"Yeah. I can't tell you how many times I've heard, 'Every baby is different' from the docs."

"Torran will have brain surgery at some point to remove the excess fluid. Dr. Ling said his head swelling is markedly increased from last week, but not enough to contact a neurosurgeon just yet because of the risks associated with the surgery.

In the meantime, they'll monitor his brain with weekly ultra-sounds and measure his head circumference. Right now, there's nothing we can do but wait."

She nods in silence. We've spent several days waiting for our boys to get better. Hope for good news is the only thing that brings us back each day.

"Listen, I had a friend make this for Nicholas because he's been through a lot and I thought you could do with a little cheering up. I know how much you liked ours."

A single teardrop falls from her eyes as she says, "Thank you." The last time I saw tears of joy was the night Torran was born.

Chairs screech on the cafeteria floor as people and leave. Bruce sits across from me, his expression as vacant as the large room. The rumpled Sunday edition of his newspaper lies on the chair beside him.

"What do you think of the chicken quesadilla?"

"It could taste like crap and I'd still love it," I answer. His colleagues started a cooking rotation. They make and freeze meals for us so we don't have to leave the hospital for supper every day. It allows us to spend more time at Torran's side.

"But it's good, right?"

"Yes, very."

"And we get Tart Man's famous treats tonight," he gives me the big toothy smile I've missed so much. Tart Man makes a mean pecan and chocolate tart. I plan on having a double serving.

We're enjoying intense relief after today's discussion with Dr. Ling about Torran's chest x-rays. She told us that she's not concerned about an infection.

The doctor explained that the ventilator caused lung damage. There is a rupture somewhere in the alveoli, the tiniest parts of his lung where oxygen comes into the body.

It's a small risk in all ventilated preemies, possibly higher in Torran because of his hypoplastic lungs. *The necessary evil of mechanical ventilation.*

Torran might develop further problems like a clot in his lungs, chronic lung disease or air getting trapped in the wrong place in his torso.

"Every baby is different," Dr. Ling responded when Bruce asked about the likelihood of Torran getting one of these problems.

We eat the best tarts in the world waiting for Murphy to make up his mind.

APRIL 01, 2008

Next to Torran's bed is a shelving unit with two zones. The lower workspace functions as a countertop. It houses Torran's medical chart, hand sanitizer, and other medical bits and pieces. The monitor displaying his vital signs rests above.

And it's shouting for attention.

Jen rushes over, her short blonde hair held back by a thin band. She rubs her hands with cleanser.

"Okay, Torran, what are you doing now?" His heart rate is under 100 beats per minute. It's happened before. This time, it isn't coming back up.

She reaches in and rubs Torran's chest with gentle pressure. If I perform a sternal rub in the emergency department, I'm trying to cause a pain response to wake someone out of a semi-conscious state.

Nothing happens. She tries again, asking her colleague to get a respiratory therapist.

"C'mon little man, pick up." Concern emerges in her voice. Bruce and I step to the side, making room for the RT Karen and her student. I stare at the heart monitor in the hopes that

I can make the numbers increase by the power of my mind. Karen demonstrates suctioning. Thick secretions come out of the tube in Torran's nose. His heart rate increases back to the acceptable rate of 150 beats per minute.

"I expected more mucous to come up," says Karen. Sometimes an excess of secretions in the ventilator tubing lowers the oxygen level or causes a low heart rate.

"He's been swinging a lot lately. I suctioned him earlier but it was really difficult to get down the tube," Jen says. "Do you want to change it and see if that helps?"

"I have an idea. His settings are pretty close to a CPAP trial. We could extubate him and see how he does."

They're talking about removing the tube in his nose. The Continuous Positive Airway Pressure machine blows a constant amount of air through a mask. Once sealed to his face, the air flows into Torran's lungs, preventing collapse; but he has to breathe on his own.

My heart rate rivals my son's. Earlier in the week, the status of his lungs was in question. Bruce and I feel like Torran is falling behind, at least in comparison to the other babies we met upon our arrival. Nicholas uses CPAP. Another preemie born on the same night as Torran breathes independently too.

I'm weary of receiving and delivering Torran's frequent bad news. When people ask, "How is he?" I want to say, "Keeping me up all night feeding"; "He poops more than any animal I know"; or "Who knew babies could make that smell?" I can't even respond that he's growing by leaps and bounds.

If I had no other reason to want a successful trial, it would be to break the monotonous daily heartbreak. More excitingly, I'll be allowed to hold him skin-to-skin. *Like a real mom.*

Karen has her student stabilize Torran's head with two hands. She applies an adhesive removing chemical under the tapes on Torran's face. It looks like they're strangling him. He struggles as they work. Shiny thin patches line his cheeks where the skin has eroded.

They slowly withdraw the long blue tube. It's covered in a thick layer of mucous. The end of Torran's nose turns up, the left nostril enlarged compared to the right. His mouth makes motions like a gasping fish. *He's crying.* There's no sound.

"The tube blocks the movement of the vocal cords," Karen says, "so it could be a few days before he finds his voice. Some babies remain hoarse for a long time." She holds a small rectangular mask up to his nose. "Let's give him a try manually first. It'll give his skin a break, too. I just want to be sure he can take the change before I go ahead and seal it on."

She holds the appliance to his face. The machine makes a quiet beep denoting the seal isn't strong enough. Bruce clamps his arm around me.

"We'll be able to tell in a few minutes if he tolerates it," Karen says, watching the monitor. She's instructing us at the same time as she tells her student what signs to observe. *C'mon, Wee Man. Please get off the vent.*

Jen's blue eyes watch the monitor in anticipation. Torran's oxygen level remains steady at 93%. Uniform waves meter out his heart beats.

Torran's miniscule chest moves up and down with shallow independent breaths. I've been concentrating so hard that I forgot to take pictures of this pivotal moment. My camera is trapped beneath his incubator. Three people surround his box, hands inside. I let the opportunity pass.

"Oh no," Jen says.

"Yeah, I see it," Karen replies calmly.

Torran's belly noticeably enlarges. The coils of bowel protrude further through the skin, making him appear more alien. Karen shakes her head.

"If I keep this on, he'll blow up like a party balloon."

I hide my whitened knuckles in my pockets. Jen sees the storm clouds in my eyes.

"I'm sorry Lesley. I know you wanted a Kangaroo cuddle, but he just can't manage it." She's holding the mask near Torran's face as Karen opens a new sterile endotracheal tube.

For the first time in my long days here, I walk away during one of Torran's procedures. If I watch Torran being intubated again, I know I'll lose what little grasp I have on my composure.

Bruce joins me in the hallway.

"Murphy strikes again."

No kidding.

YELLOW
APRIL 2 TO MAY 9, 2008

Blog Post: April 10, 2008 12:48 a.m.

Torran's One Month Birthday NICU Statistics

-born 3 months early (a whole trimester)
-weight 1040 grams at birth
-weight 1410 grams tonight (with two recent unusual big jumps of 90 grams), a difference of about 10 granola bars
-breathed 4 minutes on his own (final intubation was 10 minutes after birth) after oligohydramnios in my second trimester
-intubated 5 times to date
-4 lumbar punctures
-6 attempts for a PICC; last one successful
-5 head ultrasounds, 2 abdominal ultrasounds, 1 heart ultrasound (not to mention all the ones he had as a fetus!)
-at least 12 X-rays
-approximately 10 different tubes in either his nose or his mouth leading to his stomach
-at least 8 peripheral intravenous lines
-multiple pokes in his heels for blood tests and monitoring his blood sugar (daily)
-3 blood transfusions (Daddy can't directly donate. He's British and the blood bank doesn't want "Mad Cow Disease")
-daily caffeine doses (no rolling up rims for him)
-daily "swings" or "spells" in his oxygen and heart rate, at least 3 a day or more; spontaneously resolving and requiring nurse/RT intervention

-tolerating 7 ml/hour of breast milk (supplemented) via tube
-head circumference 28.2 cm, belly circumference 26 cm (distended), length at least 36.5 cm

Torran has been diagnosed with:
-very low birth weight
-contractures in his elbows and right knee (can't straighten)
-respiratory distress syndrome
-clinical sepsis (which nearly killed him on day 6)
-chronic lung disease of prematurity (or maybe it's PIE, they still don't know)
-grade 3 and 4 intraventricular hemorrhage (bleeds in his brain posing greater than 50% chance of left-sided paralysis)
-hydrocephalus on both sides of his brain (fluid in his brain)
-hyperglycemia, high blood sugar (now resolved)
-hyponatremia, low sodium (getting supplements)
-hyperbilirubenia and jaundice (partially resolved)
-hepatic thrombus (clot in his liver) with associated abdominal ascites (fluid in his belly)
-a 4 mm patent ductus arteriosus (you know, the one the doctor said wasn't there)

Torran has pending heart surgery, and probable
brain surgery.

I heard his voice twice; his father, at birth.
Torran appeared in two TV commercials.
He has an international fan club with members
we haven't met (but whose love and support
we cherish).
I held him for 27 non-consecutive minutes;
Daddy for 5.
I kissed him 4 times; Bruce only once.

CHAPTER 15

APRIL 02, 2008

The television mounted in the corner of my living room spoon feeds me information as I sit on the couch in my winter coat. The Toronto Transit Commission Union is in a legal strike position. YouTube Rickrolled their feature videos for an April Fool's Day prank. The CN Tower will have glass floored elevators later this month. Meteorologists forecast a warm spring.

Events unfold around me and time marches on, ignorant of my emotional distress and the tiny boy struggling to thrive. I keep the station muted, caring only about the displayed time. I stopped wearing a watch shortly after Torran was born.

Time moves like molasses when I'm with Torran. My body has its own internal settings: slow time and breast pumping time.

Bruce grabs his sleeveless flannel vest from the hall closet. He's in shorts. Must be spring.

"You ready?"

"Yep." I turn off the TV, and grab the portable breast pump disguised as a backpack. I returned the rental unit a couple of weeks ago. Renting for Torran's entire hospitalization would bankrupt me.

Before opening the door he stops. "Look, this is just a suggestion, but how about we don't watch if they're doing the head ultrasound when we arrive? I feel jittery all day afterwards."

"Yeah, sure." My sadness rumbles beneath the surface. I can't let it out. I feel like things will get a whole lot worse before they get better.

Bruce holds my face in his hands.

"I love you," he kisses my forehead. "You should ask to hold him today when they change the incubator. I like seeing you with the Wee Man."

I wish he was still inside me.

I fiddle with a tape measure during the trip downtown. It's made of a flexible plastic and easily cleans with anti-bacterial wipes. Torran's recently had unsettling gains in weight. We suspect it's not from eating.

Today I'll start independent daily measurements of his head circumference, regardless of whether or not the staff want me to. *It's my kid, after all.*

Driving to the hospital at the tail end of rush hour means that we'll miss most of the traffic and still make it for morning rounds.

The team want to get him up to a full feeding amount of seven millilitres an hour. Although Torran's bowels are moving better now, the team further investigated his abdomen looking for gut and liver infections.

One is a T.O.R.C.H.S. screening for Toxoplasmosis, Rubella, CMV, Herpes Simplex, HIV and Syphilis. I had the same test before he was born searching for the cause of his prematurity. Everything came back negative. *Still no answers.*

He had an abdominal ultrasound yesterday and we're waiting to get results.

We hit a pothole on University Avenue and I realize Bruce asked me a question. I wasn't listening.

"Sorry, what?"

"Susan wants to know if you'd like to meet Isla." Susan and Jacques are NICU Parent Buddy volunteers, an elective support program. Isla graduated from the NICU three years ago. Bruce communicates with Susan regularly. I save my energy for my blog and immediate family. *What I talk about is always so sad.*

"Uh, yeah, I don't know. I mean... No, I don't think I'm ready for that yet." Torran's barely a month old and he's endured more than Isla experienced. "I'm sure Susan means well, but I think we need a Parent Buddy whose kid had hydrocephalus, don't you?"

Bruce shrugs and makes the left hand turn that takes us to the parking lot for the hospital.

"It can't hurt. We need all the support we can get."

The doctor who couldn't look us in the eye the weekend Torran nearly died tilts her head up to our gaze. "26.2," she repeats her measurement, matching mine. "That's bigger than I'd expect it to be."

"And his weight is increasing. He's gained 25 grams since yesterday," Nancy contributes. He should gain, on average, 15 grams a day. At 24 days old, Torran is 1105 grams, about the weight of a nine week old Yorkshire Terrier. He's still within the range of "normal" for a preemie, but the rapidly increasing numbers present a concern.

The monitor warns of another drop in his heart rate and oxygen. The nurses call it "going brady" and "having swings." This apneic period when he's not breathing is called a "spell." We have the lingo down pat. Nancy prepares her hands for entering the incubator.

"OK, Slugger, what now? Showing off for your parents?" I'm glad she's back from holidays. Not all the nurses let me hold Torran during the incubator change.

The doctor regains our attention whilst Nancy negotiates with my petulant son.

"Mr. and Mrs. Donaldson, do you want the abdominal ultrasound report here or would you like to talk about it in a private room?" *It can't be that bad if we have a choice.*

"Here's fine," Bruce says. I sit in the lone chair. He puts his hand on my shoulder.

"The abdominal ultrasound's showing a blood clot in the

largest vein of his liver. It's likely that the end of the IV line in his umbilical vein pierced the liver. It happens sometimes. We can't put medication into his system to break up the clot because of the bleeds in his head."

We remain silent under our own spell as Torran recuperates from his.

"He had elevated liver enzymes in his blood tests, but those and his bilirubin levels are improving. The clot likely contributed to his jaundice. We'll do weekly abdominal ultrasounds to keep an eye on the clot. It might dissolve itself." Poor wee man. He didn't like the first ultrasound.

It must look strange to her, parents seemingly indifferent to information like this. We're not ranting about the harm someone did to our child. I'm not crying; Bruce isn't asking a flurry of questions.

We are defeated parents ruled by pessimism. If we don't get news as bad as we're expecting, then we have something positive to look forward to.

Bruce sarcastically remarks that Torran's name should be Murphy. *We're starting to re-use our jokes.* I take up my vigil at his bedside, brooding over the outcome of today's head ultrasound.

A stout man with ginger hair stands with Bruce behind my chair. He's explaining the mechanics of Torran's new ventilator. It's a different type of high frequency ventilator called a jet vent. The switch is an attempt to limit the damage in Torran's lungs.

That my newborn, unaffected by second-hand smoke and pollution, could develop *chronic* damage in 24 days is a bewilderment. Bruce asked me not to be challenging about it, as we are very happy with his care overall. However, it still befuddles me. I read a couple of journal articles suggesting that this kind of vent may not be any more beneficial. It's not hard to see why some people feel the NICU experiments on their infants.

Torran is in my arms. Nancy's granting me a ten minute hold today, so long as Torran doesn't fatigue. He's close enough to me that he can focus on the contrast of shadows in my face, the first steps of infant vision.

He draws his head back and looks at me with raised eyebrows as if to say, "Who the heck are you?" I've only seen him focus on the tube jutting out of his nose.

Torran's swaddled in blankets with more of his head exposed. He has the slimmest double chin developing. With his growing forehead, he'll soon look like a preemie Winston Churchill with flattened sides of his head. He's absolutely precious. Another RT watches the vent settings, occasionally squeezing a black bulb attached to tube in Torran's nose.

"He's not requiring all that much bagging," Nancy comments about the manual ventilation as she finishes preparing his incubator.

I feel less encouraged. "Then why can't he tolerate the CPAP if he's doing so well with this vent?"

Her answer doesn't satisfy me.

"Every baby is different. Maybe he can't handle the increased feeds and a change in breathing mode. Most babies only manage one change at a time."

"Just like his father," I say, winking at Bruce over my shoulder. He's grins in a moment of happiness.

APRIL 03, 2008

Bruce and a short black man, Anton, crowd the microwave cubby of the parent lounge. Stacy, his equally petite wife, sits in the lone chair like a forlorn child waiting for Santa to bring her a gift.

I met Stacy in the small pumping room next door. *More like the Pumping Closet.* Three mothers pump in curtain sequestered cubicles. The rest of us new-found bosom buddies line up and compare birth stories and the function of our teats, self-aware cows waiting to be milked.

Stacy, cried out in surprise when she saw the amount of milk I'd produced in fifteen minutes. She was struggling with her lactation.

"The domperidone isn't helping my let down," Stacy blurts. Domperidone increases the flow of breast milk. The quiet sigh stuck in her throat is the second sound she's made since she came into the room five minutes ago. It's amazing how women are willing to talk about their breasts to complete strangers in this place.

Our husbands chat quietly, the hum of the microwave in the kitchen cubby not loud enough to block out the booby talk.

"Right now, Savannah's only taking a few mLs at a time. It's all I can make anyways. But when she needs more... What if I fail her as a mother?" Her deep brown eyes look at me and then through me, finding her own answers.

"No way." I offer her a generic box of thin-ply hospital tissues. "You're here trying your damndest. That's what makes you a good mother. Give the medication a chance." Anton rounds the corner with a bowl of soup. Ghostly steam lifts up into the air a few inches of the surface, dissipating before it takes shape.

"I call it Dom Perignon," he says, surveying her reaction. She doesn't laugh. There isn't a muscle in her face that is free of gravity's grasp.

Savannah was born on the last day of March at 26 weeks gestation. Stacy had intrauterine growth retardation. It made her daughter smaller than expected. Doctors diagnosed Stacy with an incompetent cervix. She hates the term. I don't blame her. She felt like a failure after the miscarriage of her first child, a boy, just below that magic line of viability. The term furthers her feelings of worthlessness.

Stacy stares unseeing at the soup. Her husband balances his bowl in his hands. Bruce positions himself next to me on the solitary couch.

I invite Anton to sit next to us, then ask Stacy, "Can I meet your daughter after lunch?" Her lips pull up at the corners as her head bobs in agreement.

CHAPTER 16

APRIL 04, 2008

The blind stays closed in the stuffy pumping room. Dusty streamers of light escape through vent slats. On a worn low table, a tape-deck radio plays *Don't Stop the Music* by Rihanna. I doubt anyone here feels like dancing.

Funnels carry siphoned milk from my breasts to the storage containers attached to the pump. *It's milking time at the farm.* I've secured the mouths of the funnels in my bra. My hands, now free, multi-task to quiet the racing thoughts in my head.

Tissues at the ready, I'm updating my mother by cell phone.

"No, no, his brain cells won't grow back," I say quietly. I'm keeping my voice lowered because I don't want to freak out other mothers in the room.

"When the blood leaked from his ventricles into the surrounding tissue, it killed that part of the brain. There's fluid-filled cysts there now. The docs aren't sure if they'll get bigger or merge together."

Dr. Ling shared the news with Bruce and I this morning. It didn't give us the best start to our day. At least she respected our request and didn't offer to remove Torran's life support.

"It means that he'll be at risk for something called periventricular leukomalacia, a thinning of the white matter," I tell her. "The doc told us he's at risk for multiple problems related to brain damage." A new learning curve looms in our future. Repeating the information worsens my headache.

My mother relates a story she heard of a man who had a head scan after an injury, only to find out he was missing half of his brain.

"There's hope, Les," her tiny voice says from the speaker.

The phone's resting on the window sill as I use two hands to finish putting away my gear. "You never know what he'll be able to do."

That's the problem. Not knowing.

I don't think we can take much more. Strong people or not, Bruce and I are numb. We tried to be ready for "the worst" and it didn't work. Angry, hot tears put me to bed last night, woke me this morning, and mock me all day.

Obligated by social convention, I tell my mother she's right even though I don't completely agree with her blind faith in a brighter future. I don't share my hopelessness with anyone but Bruce.

He, too, feels like few people understand. "All parents worry," someone said to him, nearly sending him into a rant. His family member sent a card of support. We translated her words into "you made a choice that you must live with." Joel and Jeny's off the cuff saying is our daily mantra. *File things in the category of not helpful.*

"Mom, I have to go. I'm done pumping and someone else needs the space," I lie. My patience for unsolicited helpful insight is as limited as my failing energy.

As I'm rinsing the plastic in the tiny sink, Stacy eyes me closely. She was in another cubicle with struggles of her own.

"You look a little beat up." I know I'm not the cheerful woman she met the other day.

"We got more bad news today." I quickly tuck my copious milk supply in the cooler bag.

"I overheard. I'm so sorry."

"They're asking the neurosurgeon to come sooner. I just don't know if…" I have a hard time finding the words. "Ever since the beginning of this, it's been our choice… my choice, to keep Torran alive. What kind of life is that going to be?" The galley kitchenette suffocates my composure.

"Don't do that to yourself." She puts down her the tablespoon of milk she created and takes my hands. "You aren't making choices for Torran. He was already on this path. You're just helping him navigate it with the best options possible."

I have no words to answer her, only weary tears.

APRIL 06, 2008

Torran's been having more spells and no one knows the cause. Yesterday, we witnessed a possible seizure: his face became horribly slack and his eyes rolled into his head. I'd never seen that in him before. His third primary nurse, Jenn, stimulated him with manual ventilation before he came out of it. It scared the hell out of us - almost as much as meeting the neurosurgeon does today.

Dr. Francis is not what I expected for a highly specialized surgeon. He's very tall, and young in appearance. The neurosurgeon rubs his long fingers on Torran's head feeling the spaces between his skull bones, called suture lines, and the swelling at the back of his head.

"My job," he says when he finishes, "is to relieve the pressure on the brain, not just to correct the size of the ventricles." The NICU doctors showed us the vastly enlarged ventricles on Torran's ultrasound yesterday. *Two balloons in a melon.*

"Although your son's ventricles are very swollen, they aren't putting pressure on his brain because his skull plates aren't fused," Dr. Francis continues. He's seen wider splaying of the skull sutures. Most of my finger width fits in Torran's sagittal suture. He cautions us against worrying about the variation in measurements of Torran's head.

"I'm more concerned about the trend in the circumference of his head, or when it gets beyond the 98th percentile for his age group, so, larger than 31 centimetres." This man is the gatekeeper of our happiness. He's neither pulling his punches nor speaking down to us.

"If I have to, I can create a reservoir under the skin of his scalp. From there I withdraw excess fluid as often as it's required. But, that's not yet."

Bruce starts to ask a question and Dr. Francis holds up a finger to stop him. "Wait, I'm not done." I suppress a laugh. *I wish I had that power over my husband.*

"For babies this small, there's double the chance of infection, from 8 to 15%, and a much higher rate of shunt failure. I like the babies to weigh at least two kilos before surgery. The closer they are to full term, the better." Torran has at least ten weeks to go.

Dr. Francis tells us that the blood clot has a jelly-like consistency, and the cerebrospinal fluid can break it up and wash it away. If this happens, Torran won't need shunt surgery.

"What is the likelihood of this happening?" I ask, feeling hopeful for the first time since Torran's diagnosis.

"I don't sugar coat my information," he says with unwavering eye contact. "Spontaneous recovery is possible, however it's not common. Every child is different."

He briefly outlines the shunt insertion surgery, gesturing at Bruce's height. "I'll give Torran enough tubing in his belly for him to grow tall like Dad. But, I have to caution you that 99% of shunts fail in ten years because of infection, malfunction or blockage. One or all three of the components may need replacing. That being said, the first shunt I inserted is still in place."

Ten years before Torran has to go through this again? I think we can handle that. *We'll have to handle that.*

"I think I'm going to be sick. Be right back," Bruce whispers. For a second time, he leaves me alone in the movie theater.

Bruce has a headache which we attributed to our stress and lack of sleep.

Ignoring the potential migraine, Bruce suggested taking advantage of the sunny afternoon and even brighter news. Movie-going is one hobby we haven't enjoyed in months. We're celebrating Torran's delayed brain surgery.

Run Fatboy Run plays on the big screen as I happily munch the buttery popcorn. People sitting around me don't realize that my delight has nothing to do with the film.

Bruce returns, deep set lines in his face.

He leans across me without sitting down, "I couldn't do it."

"Do what?"

"Throw up. We have to go. I can't stay. Sorry." He grabs his coat and exits without waiting for my response. It's not like Bruce to leave during a film.

In the empty lobby, Bruce stands pale and unsettled.

"Honey, what is it?"

He answers only by throwing his arms around me, sobbing. The pressure of our life squeezes blood from my rock.

"Oh Brucie. It's OK." I'm afraid if I let him go, he'll fall down. My arms give him all the hugs that I cannot give our son. "Shh, sweetheart. Shh."

"I'm sorry." He repeats the apology several times. Staff members observe us at a distance.

"For what? You've no need to apologize."

"This is the first time you've had a chance to relax. I'm stopping you from watching the movie. I'm letting you down," he says in the smallest voice I've ever heard him use. "I'm so sorry."

I press my lips together over his shoulder. I don't say anything in case the tone in my voice makes him misunderstand my mirth. *Silly boy. Lovely man.* Whether or not I watch this movie isn't important.

When he calms, I kiss every part of his face ruined by grief.

"Let's go home, take time to collect our thoughts and sort out your headache. Then, if you want, we can go back downtown and tuck Torran in for the night," I suggest.

His stoicism shattered, Bruce lets me take his arm and lead him home. The other half of Simon Pegg's film runs without us.

By the time we returned to the hospital, we missed saying goodnight to Jenn. Bruce looks peaked although he recovered from his headache and nausea. I called from home to tell Jenn that we weren't going to perform Torran's six o'clock care. I didn't tell her why.

What we need before bed are Torran's lovely smiles. It might be gas, but sometimes he grins madly to a punch line only he knows. Lisa, the RT, said he looks like the poster child for intubation therapy when Torran makes his silly faces.

The wee man, active after his ten o'clock handling, accommodates his enervated parents. Torran's evening nurse hasn't worked with him before.

"Hi Mom and Dad," Hestia says. Few nurses know us by our first names, unless they work with Torran regularly. There's a serious look on her face. I can't imagine what's changed in the last few hours. "I wanted to ask if any of the other nurses mentioned hearing a murmur?"

A heart murmur means there's a hole in Torran's heart.

The thought tears one in mine.

CHAPTER 17

APRIL 08, 2008

The doctor stands in front of me, the greying hair of his knotted brows flaunting his years of experience. I have my angry face on. Bruce places his hand in the small of my back, restraining my frustration. I've just questioned this week's senior neonatologist about his decision to cancel Torran's echocardiogram.

"The heart murmur disappeared," Dr. Knutsson says, the authority in his accent unquestionable. "No one has heard it for forty-eight hours."

His logic infuriates me.

Nancy wasn't surprised that Hestia heard a murmur. "Most of our babies have a murmur before they leave here," she said earlier in the day. She drew a sketch of a Valentine shaped heart on a piece of paper and then put a vertical and a horizontal line through it.

"In the uterus, the fetus' blood flows through holes between the four chambers of the heart," she said, circling areas on the cross's lines. "At birth, pressure changes in the circulatory system make these opening close.

"A patency we often see in preemies is the ductus arteriosus, here," she indicates a bridge between two tubes jutting out of the top right-hand chamber, "between the pulmonary artery which takes blood from the heart to the lungs and the aorta which distributes it to the body.

"Think of the murmur like the sound of wind through a window," Nancy continued. "When it's wide open, you can't hear it, right? But when the opening narrows, the whine of the breeze becomes quite loud. It's the same with a PDA. A big one doesn't give off a loud murmur. It can be easy to miss."

I repeated Nancy's explanation to the doctor. His small jowl wobbles as he shakes his head in disagreement.

"If preemies are high risk for getting PDAs, then why not scan all of them?" I ask. My cheeks flush and my tone is increasingly confrontational. I don't want to be *that* mother, but I will if I must.

"Our partnership with Sick Kids focuses on babies with an identified heart murmur," he replies. *The politics of hospitals.*

"Well, Torran had one."

"For 24 hours. It may have been a mistake. It is unlikely that he would have developed a patent duct this far along. A large duct would have shown more clinical signs by now. I think the swings he's having are from the pressure in his head because of the hydrocephalus."

Nancy watches surreptitiously as she gives Torran his five millilitres meal. Maria watches the brewing confrontation from Nicholas' crib. Obstinate Me digs in her heels.

"We mentioned the bradycardia to the neurosurgeon. He doesn't think the episodes have anything to do with pressure on his brain."

"Oh. Well," Dr. Knutsson says after a short pause, "he also has very bad lungs and that contributes to the low oxygen." The doctors can't decide upon the cause of Torran's lung damage, pulmonary interstitial emphysema or chronic lung disease of prematurity. They are not the same, nor are the treatments.

Dr. Knutsson's using it as a scapegoat in his battle against me. I want to shout, "Bad lungs don't generate heart murmurs."

His puffed-up deportment remains unchanged from when we met him last week. When we met him, we tried to be jovial.

"You'll be our good luck charm. No bad news, right?" we said.

"I heard that you don't like to get bad news," came his deadpan reply. *Obviously, you misunderstand.*

"No, no," Bruce said, "we're not under any illusions. If there's information we need to know, then we'll take it." It was the wrong thing to say.

Dr. Knutsson immediately bombarded us about Torran's brain damage and the risks to his future. "It's my obligation to tell you," he concluded, "that if you wish to remove life support, it will only be available to you when your son is on the ventilator. Afterwards, that option won't be possible."

"We are *not* going to remove Torran's vent," Bruce said, undeniably firm.

Throughout the speech about Torran's uncertain future, I told myself not to listen to the doctor. *It's not like we haven't heard it before.* Later, Bruce said he did the same thing. I could almost tune out Dr. Knutsson's voice. Almost. The smallest part of me paid attention to him, in case there was a tidbit of information I needed to retain.

I wonder if he's temperamental today because I complained to Marianne, the Parent Liaison Nurse, that he violated our request about the question of life support. She spoke to him about it a couple of days ago and we've not interacted with him until now.

Dr. Knutsson stays resolute in his opinion: Torran doesn't have a PDA and he won't order an echocardiogram to prove himself correct.

Defeated, Bruce and I retreat to the solace of each other's grizzling company. Another re-heated meal neither of us tastes. He vents about the man who looks like a kind grandfather but wields power like a military general. Crying steals my voice. Again.

APRIL 09, 2008

It's early evening and I'm helping Jen with Torran's evening measurements and changing his bed linens. Torran throws his arms outwards as I lift him inside the incubator. It's a startle reflex, an infant's protective instinct.

And it's perfectly normal.

Despite the damage to his brain and the potential holes in his heart, my wee man fights to prove the doctors wrong.

He weighs 1320 grams, a little bit more than a bottle of wine. Jen documents it on a paper next to his incubator. Between it and another strip which tracks his head circumference, a little decorated sign reads "Member of the 1 Kilo Club."

"Almost three pounds. He's getting big, eh?" Jen says. Her exuberance brings sunshine into the windowless room. *But it can't chase away my clouds.*

Torran's belly is very bloated, although he poops around the clock. One night nurse said he "let out a good rip" and it decreased his abdomen circumference by two and a half centimetres.

Nutritionists and nurses tried simulating a realistic feeding pattern to let Torran's stomach decompress between meals. He couldn't digest the large non-continuous volumes. They included a human milk fortifier in breast milk. It increases his caloric and mineral intake in addition to the TPN feeding him through the PICC line.

The doctors measured albumin levels, seeking a cause for his distension. If the protein level is low in the blood, it shifts fluid from into his abdomen like a famine victim. He'll have an ultrasound tomorrow to look for free fluid between his intestinal loops. *More to worry about.*

Bruce doesn't mind my daily evaluation, although I think it makes him apprehensive. Torran's head circumference increased to 28.5 centimetres.

His head feels heavier. It's like holding a dumbbell weighted only at one end. I baby-talk to him through the plastic roof. He can't hear me over the ventilator.

How can we pull the plug on you now?

I set Torran down on the soft blankets Jen's laid out for him. She adjusts the gel-filled cushion under his head. It looks like a breast implant. They're using it to reduce pressure on his head. The medical device is very expensive and highly prized. Nurses use positioning pillows full of small foam seeds on all the preemies, keeping them him in a fetal position. It promotes healthy development. Torran's the only infant dealing with hydrocephalus, the only one with a fake boob under his head.

Jen withdraws her hand, bumping the ventilator extension tubing. The 10 centimetre length of endotracheal tube slides out of Torran's nose.

"Oh my God! I'm so sorry!" she gasps. The ventilator shrieks suitable alarms. I look from Torran to Jen's panicked eyes and my cheeks rise high on my face.

"Look at his tapes, Jen."

Jutting up from Torran's nostril, the pink tape forms a perfect tiny cylinder. To secure the endotracheal tube to his face, respiratory therapists cut a thin slit in pink waterproof tape and wrap both halves around the tube. He looks like he has an open pimple sticking out from a pink moustache.

The ridiculousness of the situation reduces both of us to giggles. Jen recruits staff to assist her. A respiratory therapist who isn't familiar with me asks me to step out for a few minutes while they work on Torran.

"I'd like to stay if I can." I'm curious to see intubation happens in infants this small. I've seen the process several times for adults. In Bruce's absence, I have the freedom to geek out over medical procedures. The RT looks at Jen quizzically.

"It's OK. She's good," Jen assures her. "Mom's an emergency nurse." *And I have the emotional strength to watch this time.*

I calmly relocate myself to the periphery of the action. I don't want to get in the way of the four people crowding around

Torran's incubator trying to get the tube back into his nose.

Unobtrusively, I snap off a few pictures for the blog. His heart rate and oxygen drop slowly. The team doesn't panic. Torran holds his own, avoiding manual ventilation. The RT holds supplemental oxygen to his face using a mask. Somewhere among the several pairs of hands in the box is the naked face of my child.

They consider trialing him on CPAP again. This time they want to use a biphasic modality. A female doctor, who joined them at some point, indicates that success isn't likely, especially with his abdominal distension.

Eventually they agree that he needs intubation. Besides, there isn't a biphasic machine available. The process proves problematic. They can't get the endotracheal tube into his right nostril.

"I don't think we've ever been able to get him on that side," Jen says. The advantage of primary nurses – they know my child as well as me. *Sometimes better.*

I can't see Torran through the wall of people. The nameless RT looks over her shoulder at me.

"Did you hear him, Mom?" she asks. The shining in her eyes tells me I've missed something important. "Come over."

The sides of the incubator have been lifted onto the top of the box. Torran lies perpendicularly across his bed. She lifts the mask away.

There is no technology on his face, or in any of his orifices. Underneath the scabs from the adhesive, Torran's cheeks have a delicate curvature. They're filling out. His nostrils flare, left more than right, where tapes and tubes chronically pulled. His tiny mouth quivers as he emits a subdued yet determined wail.

There's my wee hero.

This time, I'm not afraid to drop tears on him as I put my fingers on either side of his temples and give him a gentle upside-down kiss. The folds on his forehead kiss me back.

I wish I could listen to him all evening, but his lungs wouldn't survive my desire. The staff let me steal one more kiss before gently asking me to step aside. To save his life they have to steal his voice.

When they finish, Jen comes over to me. Her sunny grin shines brighter still.

"Are you alright?" She looks at the drying streaks on my face.

I'm a nerd. They intubated my son and it made me happy.

"Oh Jen, I heard my son!"

CHAPTER 18

APRIL 10, 2008

I throw mucous filled tissues in the garbage beside my desk. The summary post of Torran's first month was harder to write than anticipated. *Did he really go through all of that?*

My heart explodes onto the keyboard: *I don't why we were chosen for this fate. I can't tell you why our son, who is a true innocent, has to travel this road. I'll be damned if I know what lessons we are to learn from all of this. Seeing the good side of Hell is just about impossible for me.*

Each letter stares at me for five minutes. I stab the backspace key and erase them. Is it the pain of our suffering that draws people to our family story? The widget counting the blog page visitors increases daily with hits from around the world. Or are they trying to figure out how we're overcoming our sorrow?

Today is one of those weary days when I don't know if I am.

APRIL 12, 2008

For 34 days, I helped care for my baby in the box. I lifted his weightless body, changed the small diaper that engulfs him and wiped yellow crusting discharge from his eyes.

This is the first time I'm afraid to help. Jenn asked me if I wanted to turn him over onto his belly. My hand shakes.

"It's OK, you won't hurt him." She looks at me expectantly.

The spongy spaces at the back of Torran's skull make his head feel like stress-relief ball. Previously, I've moved his body and the tubes sticking out from him in unison. That was nerve wracking enough.

Jenn guides my hand placement, one hand loosely clamping

Torran's head, the other to the far underside of his body. His swollen sutures feel like warm clay sagging on my fingers.

"Now lift both your hands at the same time. As you move his torso, turn his head in the same direction."

What if I twist off his head?

She coaches me patiently as I rotate Torran's body. His legs kick out, panicked. One arm grabs at my wrist. The other wildly seeks solid ground. My heart races as fast as his waving arm.

My arms twine around him as I lay him on his belly, head facing me. I slide my hand out from underneath him. Now I can breathe.

"Good job, Lesley! Be careful, or we might put you to work."

A whole new meaning to the concept Nurse Mom.

APRIL 15, 2008

Four months after Bruce and I started dating, he went on a trip to Russia. In a tourist steam bath, he met Jay and Jenn from Toronto. They've become such close friends that today we're going to ask Jay to be Torran's "sports-mentor-father-figure."

"That, my friend, is what you had inside you at 32 weeks gestation," I say to Jenn, "minus the turkey belly and penis."

Jenn chuckles sadly, a hand sheltering her pregnant belly. She was one of many pregnant friends this year. Our babies were due within two weeks of each other. Torran should be the younger.

"So, when's the heart surgery?"

"He's on-call to go over to Sick Kids. It was supposed to be yesterday. Maybe they're letting his belly rest a bit more after his bad reaction to the medication they gave him."

Indomethacin is a non-steroidal anti-inflammatory given to premature babies to close holes in the heart. The cardiologist suggested that Torran receive a course of treatment with indomethacin for protective value regardless of the bleed in his head, the prospect of further injury being minimal.

After his first dose, Torran's abdomen blew up to a 30 centimetre circumference. With his abdomen distended up to his ribcage, he looked like he swallowed a basketball. *Murphy struck again.*

The doctors worried about a necrotizing infection in his gut. They stopped feeding him and connected his stomach to a suction pump to deflate the air. He didn't receive the additional two doses. Torran's belly resolved back to its bloating after a few days.

"He's so small to undergo surgery. I can't imagine," Jenn says, laying a gentle arm around my shoulders. Her baby inadvertently presses into me. I want to pull away.

Torran's murmur returned after my heated discussion with Dr. Knutsson. He acquiesced to the scan that would rule out the PDA once and for all.

"It's a four millimetre hole," I say, shifting my weight to the foot opposite her. She brings her arm back to her body. "They range up to five. And I accidentally found out that he has two more holes in the top and bottom chambers." The day after the echocardiogram, I read the report taped inside Torran's binder: atrial-septal defect and ventricular-septal defect.

"I told Torran that he doesn't have to get every NICU risk going, but he has selective hearing." Tonight's a night I can be lighthearted.

"You must be so mad at that doctor for arguing with you." I can see the legal wheels spinning in Jen's head, an occupational hazard.

"I'm not," I shrug. "Well, not entirely."

In the box, Torran wrinkles his forehead and opens his eyes. *Can you hear Mummy talking?*

The green see-through pacifier in his mouth dominates his

face, his tongue mauling the plastic. It's amusingly obscene. His nurses put drops of breast milk on the pacifier when they're feeding him via the syringe and tube. Tonight he really seems to enjoy it. The soother both stimulates his oral reflexes and provides self-soothing. He's been sucking on his blanket when he can get it into his mouth. In four weeks, he may be ready to start baby steps to breast feeding. *If he gets off the ventilator.*

"I'm not angry at the doctor for stating his opinion, even though it was wrong. I could've made a bigger stink about getting the test done earlier, but I didn't. A friend of mine who works with newborns equates finding murmurs to a Whack-a-Mole game."

Self-vindication seems petty now. I would rather that I was wrong, and my son's heart didn't have a problem. "Neither the doctor nor I created the opening in Torran's heart. It just ended up that way. He told me that I was right. I suppose that's his way of apologizing."

When Dr. Knutsson shared the information with me four days ago, rather than gloat, I said, "I hope the surgery improves Torran's drop in oxygen and heart rate."

"Well you know, his lungs are still really quite bad," he replied. *Can't you say something nice like, "yes, let's hope?" Or is that too much to ask?*

Bruce and I met with a pediatric brain surgeon and heart specialist in less than a week. We are numb, angry, overwhelmed and beyond sad. *How much more are we expected to take?* It seems that every time we adapt to bad news, we get sledge hammered again.

"You guys seem to be taking it pretty bravely. I don't know how you guys do it."

I touch Torran's incubator. "We have to because he has to."

We spend most of Jay and Jenn's visit reviewing Torran's turbulent hospitalization. At a nearby sushi restaurant, we have our first social dinner after Torran's birth. They listen for long spans, dampened eyes speaking volumes.

Bruce shares the latest of Torran's medical updates: a testicular hydrocele; an additional blood transfusion (accompanied by Daddy's "Mad Cow" rant); and increasing blood sugars which may herald another infection.

How much can we tell our friends before they retreat into the shelter of idle conversation? It could be their baby in the NICU instead of ours.

Our world microscopically revolves around a tiny child in an unbelievable situation. Bruce's friend in Scotland was afraid to tell us of his wife's pregnancy. Another has a niece who received third degree oil burns all over her body. The struggles of those dearest to us are not unknown to us, or judged against our own, we simply can't negotiate everyone's rainfall in the face of our own deluge. Nor can we hide our despondency. I turned down a wedding invitation because I can't repress my despair to participate in other people's happiness.

The sushi arrives at the table, and Jenn and I joke how risqué we are, one pregnant woman and one breastfeeding woman eating raw fish. Our husbands celebrate any meal choice, as long as we're the designated drivers.

"I liked what you wrote about the time machine," Jay says after we threaten many Mommy-and-wine play dates in the future. He's a short guy, but his boundless energy always carries him a few feet higher in the air.

"What was that?"

"God grant me the serenity to accept the things I cannot change, or a time machine to go back and change it," he quotes.

"I was trying to be humourous."

"But would you? Change it I mean," Jenn asks.

"I don't know why Torran was born early, so there's nothing that I could do to stop him from being born premature." This question reared its ugly head to us before. I look to Bruce. "The only choice we ever had was whether or not to let Torran live," my voice starts to crack. "We wouldn't undo that choice."

A pause hangs over the table like an old cobweb adrift in a ballroom. Bruce brushes it out of the way with his chopsticks. "You know, I go to work for stress relief from this situation. I hate it: I hate what is happening to my son; I hate that I don't know what will happen in his future, but if changing the past means Torran not being here, then there is no change to make."

With renewed spirits, I kiss the man I never imagined: a partner sticking with me on a journey I couldn't foresee.

CHAPTER 19

APRIL 16, 2008

An adapted version of "The Special Mother" from Erma Bombeck's *Motherhood: The Second Oldest Profession* displays on the computer screen, sent to me by a friend. Familiar tears fall onto my chest, tracing the rim of the pumping funnels during the early morning boobie juice session. There's not a hint of fatigue in my brain, despite returning home well past midnight.

After waiting all day, Bruce and I accompanied Torran to Sick Kids at ten o'clock in the evening. We sat in a tiny waiting room after the transfer because the staff needed time to settle him into the new NICU. We waited an hour. Torran needed more blood tests and a repeat X-ray to ensure his endotracheal tube didn't move. A painting inspired by *The Balloon Tree* decorated the wall. I counted the balloons filling the Kingdom. Twice.

I call the overnight nurse and ask about Torran before she ends her shift.

"There's nothing unusual," she reports, "I have nothing to complain about." Since I don't know the routine of this NICU, I don't know what that means. Her idea of "not unusual" may be vastly different from mine.

Bruce's alarm wakes him at 6:30.

"Morning, sweetheart," I whisper, stopping him from getting out of bed. "The nurse says there's no time booked for surgery yet, so we don't need to rush in. You can go back to sleep for another hour if you want."

Forty-five minutes later, he emerges as I'm boiling my pumping equipment. I was too tired to sterilize it last night.

"Can't sleep?"

"Fitful at best," he yawns. "Let's get going. I don't want to miss the doctor this morning. I'm not giving consent to open up my 37 day old preemie's torso by telephone."

After a rushed breakfast we head for the hospital in brooding silence.

The Atrium of Sick Kids Hospital is bright, large, and decorated with amusing characters. Bruce is impressed with its grand appearance. I was too, when I first saw it as a nursing student years ago. Now, it's just another passageway to my baby.

We arrive at the NICU as a cardiologist repeats Torran's echocardiogram for his pre-surgical work-up. To our amusement, we know this doctor. He had a daughter in the same NICU as Torran. He remembers us, and we laugh over the coincidence.

"My daughter upgraded to the Level Two yesterday," he says, standing tall. We didn't even notice that the girl left.

A vibrant Irishman in a lab coat strides into the four-bed room. We met Dr. Fitzsimmons at Sinai when he consulted on Torran's murmur.

"The Irish are taking over obstetrics and neonatology in Toronto," Bruce jokes with a toothy grin and a firm handshake. This is the fourth Irish doctor we've met since my pregnancy turned problematic. Bruce refrains from discussing European football. He's nervous despite his buoyant greeting.

Dr. Fitzsimmons takes a quick peek at the echocardiogram in progress. "At a glance, I'd estimate a 2.2 mm PDA," he says. "That's almost halfway closed!" *Bingo!* The cardiologist blinks at me, amused at my abrupt enthusiasm. In a more professional tone I continue, "The indomethacin must have worked."

"Two millimetres is still worthy of surgery," Dr. Fitzsimmons cautions. "Let me put it into perspective for you:

"The original PDA was four millimetres wide, about the

diameter of his aorta. Although it's half as big as it was, it's still quite a sizeable route for non-optimal blood flow. When the oxygen-carrying blood traveling through the aorta encounters a hole that big, a large amount of it gets shunted backwards towards the heart instead of to the rest of the body. If it doesn't close it means he won't get enough oxygen to his major organs."

"So surgery is the only option?" Bruce's shoulders sag further. I look out the pod window. Beyond, the Atrium offers respite. I will my feet to remain stationary.

"At this point, yes. I don't perform the surgery because I'm a cardiologist, not a cardiac surgeon, but I can tell you it takes about two hours from start to finish. The NICU will monitor him closely for fluid in his lungs and drops in his blood pressure. The effect of clamping the incorrect path puts sudden pressure changes into baby's system. Right now, his VSD may actually be working as a pop-off valve to help alleviate some of that excess pressure."

"Will you close the ASD and VSD? And will his hypoplastic lungs make the fluid retention worse?" I ask, the questions coming out faster and more staccato than I intend.

"I doubt whether the hypoplastic lungs contribute much to a poor recovery. At this age we don't worry about the ASD and VSD, as such. We'll see him in a year or more if he needs it. Some people live with those septal defects without a problem. I'm positive things will go well for your wee man."

With little time to digest this information after Dr. Fitzsimmons departs, a cardiac surgeon in-training seeks us out. Hands clasped in front of him, eyes glancing towards us, he's assisting in Torran's surgery. He has the consent form in his hand.

"We just open up the chest from the back, go in and clip off the open artery," he says, struggling to translate the complicated surgery in his broken English.

Maybe he's keeping his language simple because he doesn't

know who we are or how much we understand. However, this basic description lacks the eloquence of the grotesque reality Torran will endure.

Torran's ribs will be splayed apart, and his organs manipulated by grown up hands and metal tools. The surgeon must clamp shut a tiny blood vessel beside Torran's heart with stitches or clips, without cutting the wrong one or nicking other organs.

"No problem," I respond, fearing to say anything else.

I'm glad that we're standing out of hearing range of our Murphy as the surgeon obligatorily reviews the risks of surgery.

Torran's nurses at Mt. Sinai agreed that he has a talent for finding the trickiest path through the NICU. Before we left yesterday, he received a vaccination for the respiratory syncytial virus. It's a common illness in children, and potentially fatal for premature infants.

Nancy put the needle in Torran's thigh and pushed down on the syringe plunger. It didn't move.

"Oh my God. I don't believe it!" She shook her head in disbelief. The pre-filled syringe had jammed. "In twenty years, this is the second time this has happened to me. You really like small odds, don't you Sport?" She exchanged the needle, gave him more sucrose for pain and stabbed him a second time.

I know that we must hear the complications related to surgery for our informed consent, but my heart doesn't want to have more to worry about. The young surgeon refers to his illegible scrawl on the bottom of the form.

Has someone has just reviewed this with him? screams Neurotic Me.

It's a teaching hospital, replies Pragmatic Me.

He says the risks involve infection, lacerations to the vessels or lymphatic glands, the need for a chest tube to treat pneumothorax or pleural effusion ("A collapsed lung or a lung full of fluid," I interrupt to tell Bruce), nerve damage causing paralysis of his diaphragm, issues related to an imbalance in the pressures of his circulatory system, endocarditis, and a hoarse voice.

There may have been others, but my brain hit capacity. None of them are ideal. If we want Torran to live, Bruce and I must accept the consequences.

I put pen to paper, wondering whether I'm signing Torran's death warrant. The review and consent takes mere minutes. For the second time today, I want to run away crying.

By 9:30, the father-cardiologist completes his echocardiogram. He thinks the PDA is closer to 1.7 mm.

"Dr. Fitzsimmons wanted to be notified if the PDA was 1.3 or less," he says. We look at each other, not understanding what this means. "I know he has a meeting soon, but I'll page him and tell him."

Torran didn't fuss as the plastic probe pressed into his tiny body for nearly 30 minutes. I lay one hand on his bony chest. I want him to know that not all touch causes discomfort. It's sticky with the residue of ultrasound goo. My other hand cups his legs. I don't know who I'm comforting more, him or me.

Ten minutes later, Dr. Fitzsimmons returns with his boss in tow, followed immediately thereafter by a neonatologist. Bruce grips my hand. He'd step protectively in front of me if it didn't look offensive. *Three doctors. Must be bad.*

"It seems as there's been an unexpected development. Your son's PDA is at the cusp of when I would refrain from surgery," states the senior cardiologist. He's not Irish.

I know the doctors are talking because I can see their mouths moving. All my heart lets me hear are the words "no surgery." Bruce looks like he wants to hug the doctor. The tears that I wouldn't let emerge in the last hour dance down my cheeks.

"The risk of infection, in particular, makes it worth considering the alternatives," says the neonatologist. She *is* Irish.

"I'll take a look at the echocardiogram," Dr. Fitzsimmons says, "and do more in-depth imaging before I make a decision." He promises to return after his meeting to reassess the size of the PDA and examine the blood flow to Torran's brain, lungs and abdomen. If these are compromised, he'll still need surgery.

After a round of handshakes, Bruce and I embrace, alone in the small room.

"My head is spinning," his words muffle into my hair. My cheek rubs against him as I nod. "This is so confusing. And I want to be hopeful but..."

"I know, I know: Murphy."

I stand at the window in Torran's NICU pod. It opens onto the Atrium. The grand interior reminds me of a shopping mall. People crowd the cafeteria entrance. Fountains gurgle beside the empty chairs we recently occupied, guts in our chest. Behind me, Bruce stands at Torran's incubator and watches Dr. Fitzsimmons perform the last of his scans.

Ultrasound gel slimes Torran's chest, belly and head. *This kid is addicted to ultrasounds and X-rays.*

"He's got a lot of bleeding up there," the cardiologist comments as he moves the probe on Torran's head.

"Yes, we know," is Bruce's weary reply. This doctor won't bring up the topic of brain damage and life support. It's not his organ.

Dr. Fitzsimmons finishes his exam, his beaming face a stark contrast to ours.

"Your son doesn't need surgery."

I tilt my head away from Bruce, not wanting him to see my tears. The protagonist of the Australian film *Kenny* lost his son in the crowd at a big horse race and my thin shell cracked.

We're celebrating another postponed surgery at the flicks. The last time we tried this, Bruce broke down in the lobby.

Stress didn't quell his uplifted spirits today. Time lost its relativity when Torran's medical status vacillated on the fringe of heart surgery. Around 11:30, the senior cardiologist confirmed the cancellation.

They'll monitor Torran's weekly with an ultrasound. If he isn't able to get off the ventilator, has feeding intolerance or failure to thrive, it may indicate that the hole re-opened or didn't close.

As we walked through the warm April sunshine en route to the movie theatre, Bruce and I wondered if our family deserves more miracles.

"You know we won't come out of this scot free," Bruce said. I wanted to say "we might," but my heart strangled it. I witnessed Torran's possible future all around me at the children's hospital, the visible and non-visible effects of a life begun abruptly.

This is the fourth miracle of Torran's life. He was born. He breathed by himself for four minutes. He survived sepsis on his sixth day of life. Today, he doesn't need heart surgery.

Is avoiding brain surgery asking for too much?

Focusing on the absolute relief of today's narrow escape stays my melancholy. I make myself think only of one prospect: Torran at home, vibrant and happy.

And I really hope Torran likes popcorn.

CHAPTER 20

APRIL 18, 2008

The moon peeks between my bedroom curtains. I don't need my glasses to tell it's full. The fuzzy blob makes me apprehensive. In my industry, we associate full moons with disastrous shifts.

Bruce sleeps with me in the crook of his arm. I don't want to roll him over. I place my hand on the blonde fluff on his chest, feeling rather than seeing it rise and fall with his breathing. Lying with him, I feel more security than I've ever known. His arm claps around me, his subconscious not ready to relinquish his protective role.

"Go away Man in the Moon," I whisper. This is the first time in three months that I felt content when I lay down to sleep.

After Torran's cancelled surgery, we became part of the strategic miasma that plagues every hospital. Sick Kids couldn't relocate Torran back to Mt. Sinai. Technically, Torran is a patient of Mt. Sinai and the other hospital acted as consultants.

On Wednesday, as we waited to hear when and if Torran would return, the staff at Sick Kids held his feeds because they didn't know his routine, and he might transfer at any time. He received basic care and hydration as he waited.

After a day of this, Emergency Nurse Mom made several phone calls between the two units, negotiating to move her son to his previous location. Earlier today, Torran had a bumpy trip through the tunnel beneath Discovery Alley back to Mt. Sinai, what we consider his home.

"Sick Kids is a first class hospital too, and I don't mean to sound disparaging," I said to Stacy and Anton over re-heated meals in the cafeteria after Torran's return. "In some ways, I understand their logic. But, as a mother, I didn't like seeing my growing and healing son without nutritional input since he arrived there."

Little differences between the facilities escalated our internal disquiet. Between both hospitals we experienced communication problems, staffing issues, multiple births, and bed shortages. Gut wrenching.

"Quite simply, we were edgy at Sick Kids and it affected our point of view," Bruce said. "Over the last month we've developed a fairly consistent routine at Sinai. We know the staff. They know us and understand our particular needs. And they know our son. Sick Kids didn't. We felt like we had to start all over again."

"And the crappiest part," I added, "was that we couldn't get mad at things that are beyond anyone's control."

"So, we ended up with raging frustration without an adequate target."

Before we left Torran back at Mt. Sinai tonight, Lisa decreased his ventilator support. Although the tube remained in his nose, he breathed independently. He didn't have the immediate failure with the CPAP settings like last time.

I shared the news with my mother and sister as Bruce drove home. They've both been very concerned about Torran's pending heart surgery. Mom was speechless. Jessica cried.

"That's even better than him not needing heart surgery," she said. We didn't speak about my blunt words to her when she previously shared her knowledge of heart murmurs. She was right about the hospital almost missing Torran's. I hope she understands why I haven't apologized for my earlier reaction.

The unrelenting trauma we've faced stripped away nearly all my coping skills since that confrontation. Each morning I get out of bed and go through the same monotonous routine: pump, eat, dress, and leave. Sometimes Bruce and I don't speak much. We find it difficult to talk without being negative.

A world outside the NICU exists but I pay it little mind. I'm fighting to keep my head together. One day, Jes and I will sit together over a cup of tea, and I'll try to explain myself, but first I have to get through the next two months. Torran won't be coming home until June.

I kiss my sleeping prince, slowly pry myself from his arm and nudge him onto his side. My hand magnetizes to the warmth of his back.

Tomorrow I might feel like a mother.

"I love you, Wee Man," I send to the baby far away in an acrylic box. My nightly invocation has a new appeal. "Please keep breathing so I can hold you properly." I'm asleep before my tear touches the pillow.

APRIL 19, 2008

I'm sitting in a faded blue-grey armchair with a hospital gown open in the front, exposing my bra-clad chest. There's a privacy screen set up around me. At ten o'clock in the evening, Torran is active, despite the bed-time lighting. He's gripping the new apparatus on his face with exploratory zeal and he kicks the rolled blanket away from his legs.

The team removed his breathing tube and placed him and placed him on a CPAP mask before we arrived. Bruce and I helicopered over Torran waiting for an indication of failure. If Torran failed on the mask, he'd have to endure another intubation.

Premature babies don't handle multiple changes and stressors very well, and he's been through many of them in the last few days. Previously, we saw his blood sugars spike because of a minor change in his daily treatment. This week, Torran's been a trooper. He moved between two hospitals and had his routines completely disjointed, but the glucose levels didn't change.

Immediately after the switch, his nurse cautioned against the skin-to-skin "Kangaroo" hold. He slept much of the day. Torran had fatigued from handling and interventions before. The effort required for him to breathe independently could demand all of his energy. Being out of the box for an extended period of time could see him back on the ventilator.

If Nancy had said "No" to the Kangaroo hold this evening, she would've been perfectly justified. I'm relieved that her heart made her decide otherwise. A day of anxious patience paid off thanks to a nurse who performs outside of routine care yet again.

Nancy stands in front of me, holding the yellow-pink baby with the odd-looking head gear. In the right light, Torran appears lightly bronzed. The respiratory therapist, whose name I can never remember, supports the tubes dangling from his head.

"You ready?" Nancy smiles broadly, her glasses riding high on her cheeks.

"More than ever." Nancy places Torran on my chest with care.

He's lost some of the fuzzy blonde fuzz that covered his body. There is warmth to his skin that I can't sense when I lift him in the incubator or hold him in a bundle of blankets. *He feels more alive.* His toes scrunch together, a result of the effect my oligohydramnios and the oxygen probe taped to his feet. I securely cup his bottom in my hand, tucking up the skinny legs that rattle around in the diaper's leg holes.

My hand extends to the lower part of his back. His right arm splays out, the foam block and intravenous line preventing midline positioning. That arm doesn't feel like it belongs to the warm body against my skin. Torran's limbs have a little chub to them now, with soft curves instead of skeletal angles underneath sagging skin. His toes and fingers remain beautifully wrinkled. Most of the peeling skin is gone.

Nancy and the RT rearrange the multiple wires, intravenous line and CPAP tubes. I cover Torran's back with my hand, feeling the shallow respirations of The Baby Who Might Not Breathe.

I ignore the loud hiss of the air as it blows through the translucent white tube. A white cap, reminiscent of Monty Python's Mr. Gumby, holds the tubes against his forehead. Two thin tubes and one large corrugated one descend down his face, attaching to a tiny rectangular mask on his nostrils.

A fabric strap holds this piece of plastic around his head. Beneath the mask, a thick skin-like adhesive dressing prevents pressure sores. The RT assures me that the strap isn't crushing the hydrocephalus swelling at the back of his head.

Bruce takes the first picture of his wife *truly* holding his child. I don't need to check my appearance. Pure joy is my make-up.

"Look honey, a real baby," I keep my voice hushed. Bruce's Cheshire Cat grin is wider than his head.

I tuck in my chin to see Torran's face. He struggles to look up at me, the proportions of his skull and the new equipment limiting his neck movement. *Can you see your Mummy beyond those tubes?* I wish I could see through the eyes that still look like giant pupils.

"You see Wee Man? This is what happens when things are going well. I'll let you rest here as long as you want."

Torran's tongue works on the feeding tube taped to his lip. Perhaps he's instinctively seeking a nipple, now that he smells me and not disinfectant.

My connection with my frail yet resilient son deepens. It pushes all my tears aside. He's survived more than some people will ever face. All he wants in return is a chance at life.

I hum *You Are My Sunshine* because I don't know what to say to the baby who motivates me to get out of bed each day.

How do you thank your child for being alive? Although he might not hear the song above the constant *whoosh* of the CPAP, he'll feel it resonate in his chest.

Bruce places butterfly kisses on his son's head.

"Grow strong, my wee hero," he murmurs into the fuzz at the opening at the top of Torran's cap. "You're making Mummy very happy."

"Don't make me cry." The loving tone in my voice hardly makes me sound threatening.

"I'll kiss away your tears," he says in his best attempt at a heroic voice. I stick my tongue out at him.

Nancy agrees to keep Torran out of the incubator for ten more minutes. She's graciously given me a precious half an hour. *Has it been that long?* If Bruce wants to hold his son, I must relinquish him.

Without knowing what the future has in store for Torran, part of me never wants this moment to end, even though life with our baby isn't normal and I still don't feel like a real mother.

Bruce yields his time to me, but I insist that he take full advantage of this rare opportunity. *We don't know when it will come again.*

"He's so warm!" Bruce exclaims. Torran's tongue protrudes further as his fingers grasp at Bruce's chest hair, a different texture to explore. "I don't have the same pillows," chuckles Bruce as Torran fidgets.

This precious expression of love is all we want. I kneel beside my boys, banning the darkness of an unknown future from the shining peacefulness of our intimate tableau.

CHAPTER 21

APRIL 21, 2008

The city's glow warms the midnight darkness in our bedroom. A review of Torran's day fills our nightly pillow-talk. Bruce's thumb widens its arc against my hand. Kisses trail from my forehead to my mouth with increasing firmness.

"I can't sweetheart. Not yet." I don't reciprocate his desire. We haven't made love since October. *A lifetime ago.* An enormous sadness straddles my heart. I can't pull myself away from the melancholy. With murmurs of patience, Bruce lessens the urgency of his affection but not the strength of his embrace.

"Always remember, I'm so proud of you and our son," he says, lips pressed against my head. "No matter what happens each day, good or bad."

Today was one of the difficult days.

In the last month, we've made companions of some of the NICU parents. Their babies progress closer to discharge as Torran rushes headlong into a void. My spirit crushes under the differences.

Larissa went home when her twins weaned off the morphine used for her pain control. Baby Nicholas breathes without the help of machines. Mikiya, my "oligo" inspiration, was on a vent for a week. I thought Torran would have the same experience. *How naïve was I?*

Again and again we hear the phrase, "Every baby is different." Four words of best intent which feel empty.

New IV towers, ultraviolet lights and freshly weeping parents trickle into the NICU around Torran's incubator. The newest members in this hellish club are on a journey that no child and no family should face.

Some babies never come home, like the unnamed twin girl who died tonight. At least, for that much, I'm grateful for our situation. Torran's alive and fighting for his future.

Bruce feels the tears sliding between us.

"Oh, hey...why are you crying?"

"I want so badly to hold him again, Bruce!" The words rebound off the walls of our room and my heart.

After forty-eight hours of CPAP, Torran's oxygen level plummeted. The tube is back in his nose and a machine breathes for him again. Either it's too hard for Torran to breathe independently, or he's brewing an infection. Both possibilities make me cringe.

"Having Torran on my chest validated me as a mother. Now it's gone. And if he gets sick again..." I can't finish the thought, picturing that horrible day when he almost died.

"I know, my Pet." Bruce's arms can't pull me any closer. "That bloody septic work-up today worries me to death too. Five spinal taps. How much more can his little body take?" His voice waivers as he buries his face deeper into me.

Between the invasive procedures, being intubated and the return of his swelling abdomen, Torran remained fairly inactive today. He had enough energy for a few of his gorgeous smiles, as if to encourage our patience and return our love.

Quiet sobs shake my body. I want Torran to heal and be here with us more than anything. The path he must take tears me apart.

APRIL 22, 2008

We walk our customary route through the patients. *Lots of new faces today.* Nancy looks up from Torran's covered incubator. A frown superimposes itself upon her welcoming smile.

Torran's nurses work with him for twelve hours at a time.

His primary nurses know him better than anyone else in the department.

"Did Torran receive some kind of wound when I was away?" she asks, the pitch of her voice higher than usual.

Her words bring immediate alarm.

"Not that we're aware of. Why?" An uneasy tightness brews in my chest.

"Torran has a skin tear on his abdomen. I mean, it's really big. Let me show you." She moves to the far side of incubator, lifting a panel on his new custom-made tartan cover.

He's had minor skin wounds before, small areas that peeled like skin does from sunburn. The semi-circular three centimetre long skin tear gapes on the lower left quadrant of Torran's rotund belly. It ends in a tapering point as if the top layers of skin were pulled away from his midline, like someone removing a probe. A thin layer of blood and serum glisten on the shallow surface.

"I don't know where it came from," Nancy says. I've never heard her distressed before. "There's nothing about it in his nursing note. Something like this should be documented, but there's no mention of it."

She opens the thick tome at his bedside and reviews the most recent entries. "See, here, his IV went interstitial and it was replaced." That's typical for Torran. His IVs never last more than a few days. She pointed out the notation of dip in his heart rate. "But there's nothing about a skin tear."

Bruce's brow furrows. "It wasn't there when Lesley changed him at six in the evening. I think Jen would've said something if it happened before she left."

"I think it's painful for him. He grimaced when I cleansed it with saline and he's fussier than usual." Nancy's eyes dart from documentation to Torran.

Accidents happen, but they shouldn't be ignored. I don't

know what perturbs me more, the apparent disregard for this injury, or that I can't pick Torran up and soothe him.

"I want to let him rest for now," Nancy says. "He's having his first eye exam this morning, and the babies never like it. We always have problems with swings afterwards."

She says the procedure starts with freezing and dilating drops in the eyes. The babies' eyes are forced open. The fluid stings. An hour later, an eye specialist comes from Sick Kids with special forceps, pries the eyelids open, and uses a bright light and lens to view the retina at the back of the eyeball.

"The opthalmologist looks for retinopathy of prematurity, nerve damage in the eye," Nancy says as she puts Torran's records away. "ROP is caused by exposure to the oxygen we deliver. The babies might need laser surgery to correct it. Sometimes they go home blind."

Torran, oblivious to the upcoming torture, sleeps in his box. *Paralysed and blind. What are we doing to you?* Staying focused on The Now proves more challenging than worrying about The Future.

"You might have to take a pass on cuddle time today." I won't question her about the advice. If Nancy thinks Torran needs the rest, I'll follow her instructions and ache a little bit longer.

She turns to collect frozen breast milk and nearly bumps into a man my height with tight grey and black curls and squared-off glasses. He introduces himself as Dr. O'Connor, another senior neonatologist. *Irish.*

Nancy conveys her concern about Torran's skin tear and its effect on the wee man. Dr. O'Connor agrees that the recent flurry of activity and the wound may cause Torran too much stress. He endorses a day of rest. Then he begins his review of Torran's care plan.

"He's 32 weeks, 1630 grams and not at full feeding volumes. I'd like to improve that." His gentle tone gives reassurance.

"We'll increase his caffeine doses to stimulate his breathing and try to get him up to full feeds at the same time.

"I'd also like to pull back on the amount of imaging. Torran's neurological status is pretty good. The head swelling hasn't changed dramatically and the brain ultrasounds are pretty consistent. The same is true of the fluid in his abdomen and the clot in his liver."

"What about the PDA?" Bruce asks. "The cardiologist said there's a slim possibility it could re-open."

Dr. O'Connor thoughtfully strokes his wiry beard. "To be honest folks, if Torran isn't changing in his presentation and the echo shows that the PDA is the same size, we're not going to rush him off for surgery." Our heads bob in agreement. "These things usually don't close until regular babies reach forty weeks gestation. Sometimes the best treatment is to do this..."

He places his hands over his eyes.

APRIL 23, 2008

Be brave. Smile, even if you don't want to.

Bruce's friend Shirley gave birth to her daughter as we watched Torran struggle through his day. Shirley and her husband Gary invited us to the 10th floor to meet Shannah. I make the expected congratulatory greetings as we enter.

This maternity ward has a significantly different feel to that of the high risk prenatal unit on the 7th floor. There aren't any pictures of intubated or skeletal babies on the walls. Doorways lack the quiet groupings of petrified families. Smiles, flowers and balloons fill the halls. Shirley's room seems somehow wrong. I was in a room like this one three floors down, but it was missing a baby.

As Shirley gave birth, I unsuccessfully held my son.

At the end of the day yesterday, Nancy let me hold Torran,

although she didn't want to risk it skin-to-skin. Instead, I held him wrapped up in blankets on top of a pillow in my lap, the ventilator tube jutting out from his nose as it does in the incubator.

I thought it was a harmless surface for him, more comfortable than the box. I was wrong. Moments later, his oxygen level dropped with another period of apnea. He barely digested two millilitres of his ten millilitre milk volume.

Torran couldn't eat, breathe, and be with me.

I returned him to Nancy, rejected. She stimulated his breathing. Today Nancy offered me another try. I declined. He needs rest more than I need cuddles.

Shannah weighs eight pounds; Torran times two. Her head and body are bigger than his. I give our friend a hug and gingerly caress her giant baby's back. Shannah, feeding at her mother's breast, is perfect – perfectly on time and perfectly formed.

APRIL 25, 2008

The phone rings. I levitate four feet above the mattress from an unsound sleep. *Oh no. It's the hospital. Oh no. It's the hospital. Something's wrong. Something's wrong.*

It can't be infection, because the tests came back negative. Did we tire him out with our cuddles in the evening? He looked uncomfortable as we held him. Did we hurt his brain by putting pressure on the back of his head?

"Hello? Hello?"

Blank air. Beep. White noise. Beep.

If I didn't like automated telesales before, then I sure as hell have no patience for them now!

I spend the rest of my night in twilight, the phone one foot from my grasp.

APRIL 26, 2008

Little outfits. Cuddly toys. Soft rattles. I'm looking for newborn gifts for the recently popped out healthy, full-term, uncomplicated newborns of our friends. I skipped their baby showers by choice. Torran never had one. *I don't know why I'm torturing myself here.*

I turn a nine ounce bottle over in my hands, amazed at the volume it holds. Torran digests less than a 9th of that amount. Torran chose eating over breathing. He couldn't increase his feeds and breathe at the same time. We'll keep him on the ventilator for the weekend and let his body ease into full doses of milk. He's eaten so little. The nurses give him milk I produced almost a month ago. We saved the rest in a freezer purchased using a monetary collection from my colleagues. *I'm a dairy queen.*

Shopping thrusts me into the real world and smacks me upside the head. I see the brass ring - a healthy baby - out of my reach everywhere I go. *Only the NICU feels safe.*

Nancy and I are no further along in understanding the origin of Torran's skin tear. Jen knew nothing of it. I spoke with the overnight nurse during an early morning pumping session by phone from home.

The skin tear was present before her shift, she claimed. I pressed her hard for credible information, knowing that such a large injury on a delicate baby should be documented and monitored. There was none.

The woman related the tragedy of her infant's death to my situation, suggesting that it's difficult for a medical professional to trust others in a role reversal. It infuriated me. I wanted to throw the phone across the room when the futile conversation ended. With Bruce sleeping in the next room, my anger was left as unsatisfied as the answers I sought.

Weariness skulks around my thoughts with frustration as a bosom companion. In the unit, I avoid that nurse for fear of what I might say. I won't let her be Torran's nurse.

Bruce and I returned to the coping strategy we adopted in Torran's first week: a stable day is a good day. Our emotionally guarded days grind, exhaust, and overwhelm us.

We remind ourselves of his accomplishments regularly. Otherwise, we feel like he's no better off than when he arrived.

Our little family... what happens if our strength and optimism fail? Thinking of it makes me shudder.

I select one of the bedding sets for our friend's gift. The NICU's first step towards normality mocks us. Torran's age and weight make him big enough for a crib. However, they won't put him in there until he's securely off the ventilator.

A big boy bed...

Big boy. That's a relative term.

CHAPTER 22

APRIL 28, 2008

Four plastic collection bottles rattle together in the boiling water. I rotate the surfaces with a metal spoon. This daily observance changes little. Sterilizing breast pump equipment in a pot seems antiquated compared to the technology we've used on Torran.

A bubble on the surface explodes, throwing a large drop of water on my hovering hand.

"Dammit!" The burn adds to my edginess. I'm running behind and I've missed Torran's morning rounds. *They're going to mess up the plan.*

Torran's primary nurses devised a scheme for simultaneously increasing his dietary intake and improving his breathing. His care police, those fantastic primary nurses, want him weaned more slowly than other babies. On the other hand, the RTs and doctors itch to get Torran off the vent.

The tip-toeing around his status meant an extra week of us waiting to hold him skin to skin, but it was a sacrifice Bruce and I were willing to make. Yesterday, Torran managed a three hour cuddle wrapped in blankets.

On Saturday, the doctors started weaning Torran off the ventilator early. The speed of the changes unnerved me. Introducing CPAP too soon could undo all the primary nurses' week long efforts.

It's time to be Pushy Mom. I call the hospital and tell Torran's nurse that I don't want him off the ventilator before I arrive.

A few hours later, I walk to his incubator, making my customary glance at the surrounding equipment. A new breathing machine immediately catches my attention. I lift the blanket on the box. The ventilator tube is still in his nose. *What's going on?*

Today's nurse, Jullie-with-two-Ls explains. "He's breathing on his own with a little bit of pressure support to keep his lungs inflated. He's on CPAP settings through the tube instead of a mask."

"What? No! We weren't going to trial him on CPAP until he's back with his primary nurse tonight." In my rush to re-establish some kind of control over the situation, Jullie might infer that I think she's less capable. *I don't care.*

"I'll keep a close eye on him," she says, "especially after that episode he had on Sunday." That day, Torran's heart rate shot up to 196 beats per minute and he looked like he was gasping for air after Jullie repositioned him. When she adjusted him again, the gulping motions stopped and his heart rate decreased slightly, but he had trouble keeping his oxygen up.

Additionally, we saw signs of pressure on his brain. His eyes rolled downwards, what Dr. Unger, another staff neonatologist, called "sun down" eyes. I have no idea if it causes Torran discomfort. *It hurts to look at him.*

Dr. Unger wants Torran off the ventilator despite my concerns about rushing his breathing. To her credit, she's keen on updating us about Torran's recent brain ultrasound and obtaining a re-assessment from Sick Kids. I don't know how to feel about the assertiveness of the brunette. On one hand, she's not a "yes" woman to my anxiety; on the other, she's focused on Torran's improvement.

My emotion and intellect cycle rapidly like the colour in Torran's face when he's bearing down.

Yay! He's breathing on his own. *They've pushed him too hard.* He's still intubated. *This contradicts the plan.* The vent can be re-started if needed. *I'm so proud of you, Wee Man.* If he fatigues the tube is already present. *Please don't tire out.* We have to create a new game plan now. *Is it too hard to breathe through the straw on your own?* He lasted forty-eight hours last time. *How long can he stay like this?* Is he indrawing too much? *Am I being too cautious?* They've pushed him too hard.

"Well, that's that," Jenn says as she helps RT slide the long tube out of Torran's lungs. "He's flying solo."

Bruce and I clasp damp palms as they secure the adherent dressing to his face and cover his nostrils with the small mask. I refused Dr. Unger's request to remove it earlier during the day. I want a primary nurse to watch him tonight after this strategic step.

They swap out the machines. I grit my teeth as my anxiety increases.

"Lesley, he's going to be OK," Jenn says, giving me a hug when her hands are free.

I place a sweaty palm on the plastic wall and hold my breath as I beg for this next step to work. Torran's frail chest rises and falls, tiny puffs of air racing in and out of a ribcage no bigger than a chicken's. The motion is so simple for a process that is so complicated. *Please don't fail, Wee Man.*

APRIL 29, 2008

The smell of pizza overpowers the scent of hospital cleansers in the corridor as I approach the 7th floor classroom. Every Tuesday, the NICU social work department at Mt. Sinai provides an evening meal and informational session for parents.

Tonight they're showing a film about coping. Marianne co-chairs these meetings. She invited me to "come for the pizza." She looks like a stereotypical librarian with her short greying hair and glasses, but her expressive hand gestures give her the flair of an actress.

I pause at the door. The pizza smells more appetizing than my sandwich from home. There's a green and white poster advertising a NICU charity walk-a-thon at the end of May. It's a rapidly warming spring. *Maybe by then I'll want to go outside.*

Still undecided about whether or not I'll stay for the session, I pull the door open and take a deep breath. Inside sit the most stressed collection of parents I've ever seen. Maria's alone too. I grab a slice of pizza and join her.

The social worker assigned to our family, Helena, gives a warm welcome. Going around the room, we introduce ourselves and our babies. *Hi, I'm Lesley and I'm a failed uterus.*

Maria and I are the matrons of the group. Our children are the oldest, born 7 weeks ago. The youngest is 8 days old. NICU babies have two ages, the number of days they've been alive and the number of weeks gestation they would've been if they were still in the womb. It's called a corrected age. *And it's a painful reminder.*

Helena and Marianne explain that the sentiments in the 1980's American movie for this evening's meeting are universal and contemporary. Keeping my tears at bay, I watch the documentary with heart-tugging pensiveness. In the last scene, a crying mother describes her financial sacrifice. She sold everything but her mobile home and a car to pay a quarter of a million dollars in medical bills.

"But it was all worth it."

Her words bond the crumbling seams of my heart.

Helena invites feedback from the group. Instead of opening up about our feelings, we sit in a long uncomfortable silence.

Suddenly, a muscular man taller than Bruce expresses his frustrations over a doctor's delivery of negative information. It offended him when the doctor offered to remove his baby's life support. His arms accent his sentences like a Musketeer.

Embers of his anger resonate with Maria and I. He's been

struck with a powerlessness that he cannot comprehend. For his barely viable baby, every moment is a fight for survival with an unknown outcome.

But, I also have a sense of cold detachment. I didn't like being told that Torran might die or have a lifetime of disability, but what other option did the doctors have? Bruce and I felt that we brought Torran into the world and it's our responsibility to give him as much as we can. Not every parent feels the same. That's the harsh reality the doctors face.

Choosing suffering is complicated.

Through each of our difficult days, we coast on Torran's tenacity for life. Until the wee man shows otherwise, Torran's weary parents pull our armor on every day and enter the battlefield for his sake.

Today's armor came with pizza.

APRIL 30, 2008

For seven weeks and three days I've sat at this shrine and dedicated my soul to a pint-sized god. I'm weary. My heart is threadbare. I don't feel like the well meaning people around me truly understand. My faith, a tattered remnant that marches me to daily invocation, suffocates in the artificial womb in front of me. Torran's tiny, rapid breaths set the rhythm of my thoughts, the pace of my hope.

And they're all his own.

He's had swings in his numbers. Each time he couldn't recover on his own, my heart twisted. *It didn't break.* He succeeded the transition to CPAP.

I reach my hand into one of the incubator doors and infuse my love through the delicate touch of my fingertip in his hand.

"Breathing is hard work and nobody realises it. What do you think, Wee Man? Can you handle a cuddle with Mummy?"

Torran lies with his head turned to one side, staring at me. His smiles, ready to receive my offerings. My worship for his stability. That's a fair trade.

CHAPTER 23

MAY 01, 2008

Bruce bends over, tears in his eyes as he laughs. He tries to stop, sputters, then loses control of himself again for another five minutes. This isn't unusual for my husband.

Torran immediately christened his new big boy crib with projectile poop, some of which landed on my hand. Enjoying toilet humour also isn't unusual for my husband.

Having Torran in a crib feels like a bigger preemie achievement than avoiding heart surgery. We're closer to being real parents. The crib is a large, metallic bed suitable for the set of a scary movie. There's no salad bar sneeze guard between us and our son. We can kiss Torran as much as we like, although finding his face behind the CPAP mask is more difficult than I realize.

Yesterday, we took turns holding Torran for four hours in a Kangaroo cuddle without fatiguing him. He wriggled as he explored the warmth of Bruce's chest.

"Life outside the box is going to be a whole lot of awesome, Wee Man," I say as I dress him in one his first baby outfits.

When Torran was in the incubator, we changed his diaper and placed a thermometer probe in his armpit. We put the syringe of food on the feeding tube. I'd measure his growing head circumference and help weigh him during the evening linen change. Now, holding oxygen to his face, we're learning to bathe him (how slippery!) in a basin on a counter-top instead of wiping his body with damp tissues inside the incubator.

"Yeah, this isn't his colour," Jenn says. She straightens the yellow fabric across his body. Sized for a preemie, it remains too big on him. Yellow emphasises Torran's lingering jaundice.

There's still so much that we're asking of our wee hero. Beyond our concerns about his hydrocephalus and brain damage, Torran must learn to self-regulate his body temperature, breathe independently, and co-ordinate breathing and eating.

Yet, this moment of immature humour and novice parental awkwardness masks those fears. Bruce's laughter darns the smaller holes in our hearts.

MAY 04, 2008

An ocean of afternoon sunshine dances on Lake Ontario as we drive along the Gardiner Expressway. The bike path splits the greening verge. Birds swoop from a lamp, investigating the spring bugs alongside the road.

I turn from the vista and check the drivers around us. So far, I'm getting away with my portable breast pumping experiment. The police haven't pulled us over for indecent exposure and we haven't caused any car accidents.

We're meeting Keith and Carol, friends from Burlington, at the hospital. Our routine makes scheduling visitations tricky, so I decided to pump en route in the front seat of the car.

A silver truck blocks my view. The tall, grey-bearded driver leers at me. He sees directly into our smaller car. I'm partially covered up, but from his vantage point, it's obvious I'm doing something weird with my breasts. A woman leans over him with her thumbs up.

From deep within, jubilant energy erupts.

"What's so funny?" Bruce asks of my uncontrollable guffaw.

"Look beside me."

Bruce glances at the vehicle pacing ours. "Of all the..." he starts, similarly infected.

Keith and Carol cheer from the front seat.

The incline of Torran's crib keeps his infantile beer belly away from his lungs. After nearly eight weeks of having a tube blocking his vocal cords, he recovered a faint, hoarse voice. When he cries loudly, it sounds like the quiet fussing noises of a normal baby.

"Hello Peanut," Carol greets Torran softly as she kisses his head. Keith reaches in from the other side of the crib. Torran's hand barely encloses his forefinger.

"I know we haven't seen your Mommy for a long time, but everyone follows your news. And look, we made you a special belt favour. Silver for the anniversary," Carol says of the embroidered bear on a piece of rectangular fabric. It represents our branch of The Society for Creative Anachronism, a medieval re-enactment group.

I take their gift and add it to Torran's small collection of inspirational tokens: a prayer card and holographic religious symbol from our next-door neighbours, a St. Christopher's medal from my sister, and a bookmark from my unicorn collection. A hope-bead bracelet travels with me. The bookmark reads: anything is possible if you only believe.

In the half an hour standing at Torran's bedside, they never break contact with him. As with our few visitors before, they stand in silence as we recount his tribulations. When I can't continue, Bruce takes over seamlessly.

Torran's face turns dark blue as he bears down with a silent grunt. His stupendous belly swells. An alarm chirps as his heart rate and oxygen level fall.

Carol leans back, looking to me for direction. Keith surveys Torran and the equipment with a discerning eye. He's a police dispatcher and not prone to panic.

"The bradycardia happens when Torran increases his abdominal pressure," Bruce says, the medical language now second nature to him. "It usually stops when he relaxes." Torran begins breathing again. The colour returns to his face.

"How often does *that* happen?" Keith asks, eyebrows raised.

"Multiple times a day, every day," I say, fussing aimlessly with the plastic bag at the end of Torran's bed. The bag of good wishes that hung on the outside of his incubator now lies at the end of his bed. We're not allowed to affix anything to the crib rails or put anything inside that isn't easily wiped with disinfectant. *No cute stuffies for you.*

Infection control is a rigorous discipline in the NICU. My hands are raw and bleeding from hand washing and alcohol rinse. Keith and Carol struggled to remove rings they'd never taken off before when washing their hands at the communal sink outside. The NICU policy forbids hand and wrist jewelry under which the microbes grow.

"He's looks so good," Carol ignores the mask on his face. She marvels at Torran's diminutive size. "Hard to believe that one day he'll be big like Bruce. Does this mean he's done with the ventilator?"

"That's what we're hoping, but each day is a waiting game. He's recently been showing signs of tiring out," I reply. "Yesterday, the doctors increased his caffeine dose to a maximum amount." We're on tenterhooks waiting for him to fail again.

"Good thing Tim's is having their Roll Up contest," jokes Keith. "There's lots of caffeine to go around."

Bruce snorts derisively. "For the amount of Tim's we've bought by being here, we've won very little. And no car."

"I'm lucky in love," I add, "not lotteries."

"So what's the next step for him?" Carol asks.

"He's learning how to breathe by himself now." I try to keep my voice calm. "Sometimes he forgets. The episodes are worse when he's trying to digest the milk they put through the tube." I don't want to jinx myself by mentioning the risk of re-intubation.

As if on cue, the alarm sounds off again. This time, our Murphy's not bearing down. His heart rate drops dangerously low. I drop the side rail and tickle Torran's clothed feet.

"C'mon, Wee Man, don't misbehave just because we have visitors," I plead. His dusky colour persists as the oxygen level slides to 85%. "Bruce, you need to get the nurse." He rushes to the main desk. Carol joins her husband on the other side of the crib.

I rub Torran's chest vigorously like I've seen the nurses and RTs do during earlier episodes of prolonged apnea.

He doesn't start breathing.

Torran's nurse arrives and I yield my spot to her expert attentions. Anna's not one of his primaries, but she's equally competent with his care. She quickly sets up equipment for manual ventilation of his lungs.

Lisa, hair hastily pulled back in a ponytail adjusts settings on the CPAP machine. She shakes her head in frustration. The numbers refuse to budge.

"We don't have much leeway here," she explains. "I've upped his oxygen as much as possible. As much as I hate to say it, if he's tiring out, we'll have to put him back on the vent." Pink hues with an undertone of yellow slowly emerge in Torran's skin. "Let's give him half an hour and see what happens."

Hot tears reveal my insecure heart. I can't bear to tell my friends what this means.

"Maybe we should give them some space. Let's try to win a coffee downstairs," Bruce says, seeing the unspoken words on my face. He knows what I'm thinking.

Carol, her strength outweighing her stature, takes my arm and leads me from the boy who's increasingly surrounded by faceless people in scrubs. We hold each other in the elevator in silence. There will be tears instead of laughter on her ride home.

Four parents ride the elevator to the ground floor, their babies upstairs, tucked in for the night with an abundance of kisses on their heads. Stacy, Anton, Bruce and I weave through the after-hours security barriers, leaving our children and our hearts behind.

"I think all our kids got together last night and decided to stage a coup d'état," Anton jokes as we head to the parking lot. Several children, including Torran, kept the staff busy today.

A baby born the same night as Torran, and who progressed to Level 2 a few days ago, returned to the Level 3 accompanied by tearful parents. A third baby in our corner abruptly encountered problems when previously she had steady improvement.

Savannah kicked out the intravenous line in her foot whilst Stacy was holding her. Blood spilled everywhere. She's being treated for meningitis, an infection in her brain.

"I think I'm going to have nightmares about that IV in Savannah's scalp," Stacy says. The polished appearance she regained in the last few weeks is completely shattered by this one event.

Carol and Keith shortened their visit allowing Bruce and I to stay with Torran without worrying about entertaining them. Lisa managed to stabilize him for an hour. We spent an anxious evening pacing each minute, waiting for Torran to decide if he was too tired to breathe by himself, maxed out everything the team could give him.

At 6:00 p.m., the next big challenged arrived. When digesting the breast milk, Torran had one small dip in his status. Anna didn't feel as though it was enough to put him back on the ventilator.

We're glad she waited. After the evening shift change, blonde Jen joined us. She noticed his feeding tube was two centimetres out of place. It might have been a contributory factor to the spells.

He settled down after she adjusted it, but we're leaving him with his machines remain at the highest settings.

Doubt prickles on our nerves. Like Stacy and Anton, we head home, rubbing elbows with stress and worry like old friends.

GREEN

MAY 10 TO JUNE 10, 2008

Blog Post: May 10, 2008 10:32 p.m.

Torran's Two Month NICU Statistics

-born 3 months early; he is currently 61 days
old, 35 weeks + 4 days "corrected"
-weight 1040 grams at birth - approximately
2 lbs 5 oz
-weight 2520 grams tonight - approximately
5 lbs 6 oz
-breathed 4 minutes on his own at birth
-intubated 7 times to date
-9 lumbar punctures
-6 attempts for his PICC
-9 head ultrasounds
-4 abdominal ultrasounds
-3 heart ultrasounds
-at least 15 X-rays of his chest and belly
-approximately 20 different tubes in his face
for feeding and/or suctioning
-at least 12 peripheral intravenous lines
-over 60 heel pokes
-4 blood transfusions
-daily caffeine doses
-large exudate of commensal flora in both ears
-many pressure sores on his skin
-daily "swings" of low oxygen and heart rate
not requiring nursing intervention
-an average of 1-2 "spells" per day requiring
nursing intervention
-tolerating 42+ mL of breast milk every
3 hours, supplemented with human milk
fortifier (a kind of formula)

-head circumference 34.4 cm (90th something percentile... bigger than average)
-belly circumference 35 cm (much bigger than average and very full of air)
-passed two eye tests for retinopathy of prematurity
-one large idiopathic skin tear, and bunches of little ones
-on his eighth week he came off and stayed of the ventilator, with the use of CPAP to maintain his lung pressure, and the delivery of oxygen
-he's been breathing on his own consistently for 13 days; prior to that only for 48 hrs

Torran has been diagnosed with:
-very low birth weight
-contractures in his elbows and right knee
-respiratory distress syndrome and hypoplastic lungs
-clinical sepsis
-chronic lung disease of prematurity
-grade 3 and 4 intraventricular hemorrhage in his brain
-hydrocephalus on both sides of his brain
-hyperglycemia (now resolved but he still has problems balancing his blood sugar when they change the recipe of his fortifier)
-hyponatremia
-hyperbilirubenia and jaundice
-PDA (1.7 mm 3 weeks ago), ASD and VSD
-hepatic thrombus and ascites
-hydrocele (swelling in his testicles)

-umbilical hernia (protrusion of the inside of his abdomen through his belly button)
-perianal skin abrasion, now healed
-anemia (low haemoglobin - takes iron supplement)
-biochemial osteopenia (low bone density - takes calcium and phosphate supplements)

Torran may have brain surgery in the near future (1-2 months) to insert a shunt.
After three weeks of holding it in, followed by two and half more weeks of interfering medical issues, he is finally pooping like a trooper.
He appeared in two commercials, and two news segments.
He transitioned to a crib 52 days after birth.
Smiles he shares in abundance, although less often on the CPAP because he's tired.
He rapidly accumulates lots of mummy and daddy kisses.
He latched onto my breast twice in learning to feed, although the second episode only for a minute.
Three immunizations have been given by needle into his legs (two tonight).
He enjoyed three baths in the big boy bathtub; one in the salad bowl.
Of his 1440 hours of life, we have cuddled him in our arms for approximately 20 hours.

CHAPTER 24

MAY 11, 2008

My warrior sleeps beneath a tented black and white sheet, oblivious to the significance of today and the increased number of visitors in the NICU. The contrasting squares in the checkered fabric stimulate his vision. It causes the nurses headaches.

As of May 6th, Torran doubled his birth weight. He's now a whopping 2270 grams. My five pound boy has a head circumference of 34.4 centimetres. *Almost at surgery size.* Ultrasounds show that the swelling inside his brain hasn't changed much, but Bruce and I hope the surgeon will re-assess Torran soon. He's started "sun-downing" again.

"What's this?" Nancy asks as she opens the mint green envelope I handed her.

"You'll see." My face won't reveal its secret.

Nancy's eyes glisten as she reads the sentiments within the card - a Mother's Day card for her from me.

"But you're his mother." She wipes her eye as discretely as possible. She picks at fluff from her dragonfly patterned scrub top. "This really isn't necessary."

"Yes, Nancy, it is." I place my hand over hers. "You, Jen and Jenn are as much mother to Torran as I am right now. You feed him and change him, cuddle him when he's crying and coo over him when he isn't. You worry about him when you leave. You're doing all the things that I want to do - that I would be doing if he was at home."

"No one has ever done this for me before. Thank you."

In their endearing attachment to Torran, these women protect him from harm, promote his growth, and bring him closer to his home and his parents. None of his primary nurses have children of their own. There is no simpler way to express our gratitude than giving this Mother's Day to them.

As she tries settling Torran in my arms, Nancy's face pinches, although she's trying hard to hide it. She fretfully rearranges the lie of the lines and tubes emerging from Torran and his clothes. They've become trapped on my right arm as I hold him in a new position, like a football.

"An American football," Bruce would correct me, were he here instead of at work. The NICU doesn't usually put babies to a mother's breast when CPAP is in use. However, Dr. Unger was determined to start Torran on the steps to breast feeding, CPAP mask or no.

"Other hospitals are having some success with the bigger babies being introduced to breast feeding before coming off the machine. I know there's a risk for inhaling his food and getting aspiration pneumonia. But, Torran is 35 weeks corrected age, and it's time for him be a big boy. He's still got a long way to go. We need to motivate him."

I happily agreed to the quasi-experimental breast feeding. Yesterday, Jen, like Nancy, was less confident in the unusual process. Torran squints at me like he's trying to figure out who I am from this angle. Clichéd pick up lines run through my head.

For fear of squishing his brain, his primary nurses haven't secured the CPAP mask too tightly. He's lacking the bug eyes we've seen in Savannah from CPAP strap. The deafening hissing sound is the same.

I'm so excited, I nearly forget about the troubles with his skin. The pale blue onesie conceals the beginnings of a scar from the puzzling skin tear. There's a new excoriation at his buttocks from unusually frequent stools.

Infant poop looks like yellow liquid with pellets of yellow stuff the texture of cheese curds. The concern about diarrhea puts us back on abdominal infection watch again. His 35 centimetre belly has its own preemie postal code. Last night a nurse blew oxygen on his sore bottom to promote skin healing. *A different kind of gas at his bum.*

I doggedly encouraged Nancy to try this new skill. Torran and I start with a technique called non-nutritive sucking. After pumping out all the milk, I put him to my empty breast. Then he won't inadvertently get milk in his mouth and choke.

I fumble with the awkwardness of handling my child as well as the attachments on his head. A lactation consultant named Naveen supervises each step. My desire for success overlooks her hands in my personal space.

My head spins with the thought of the number of things that must happen for this "natural" part of motherhood to be successful. Torran needs a rooting reflex, the ability to find a nipple and latch successfully. No one can teach him the skill of sucking milk from me.

"And," Naveeen says, her pile of information building higher, "he'll have to get used to the feeling of breast milk shooting into the back of his throat."

Moreover, he must learn how to eat and breathe and swallow all at the same time. *I feel like we've been here before.*

When Stacy tried Savannah at breast feeding, all she did was sniff, lick and fall asleep. Torran comes at me like a starving man.

While he's eagerly munching on an empty breast, Nancy puts defrosted milk into Torran's stomach using the tube. "This way he'll associate feeding with your body." His machines remain mercifully silent. Nancy glows with pride as she looks at her surrogate son. The last half syringe of milk empties into his belly as he sleeps bundled against me.

Breast feeding is the only part of mothering Torran that belongs solely to me. It's our unique method of bonding. Thanks to the persistance of Dr. Unger, I'll have better Mother's Days in the future.

MAY 13, 2008

There was a tornado in the State of Georgia on Mother's Day. A storm's been brewing in the NICU since then. The lights of the CN Tower shrink as I drive home by myself, leaving the NICU, but not my thoughts, behind.

Today's events and a growing loneliness agitate my brewing moodiness. Bruce has a cold. It's a simple sniffle, but he won't bring it to the hospital. He's miserable about missing Torran. However, we discouraged my mother from visiting when she didn't feel perfectly healthy. Bruce doesn't want to be a hypocrite. Ironically, the topic for this week's parent information session is "Infection Prevention."

Torran stopped breast feeding. I can't figure out a cause. He's fussing far more than usual. His alarms went off frequently. The nurses had to take a step backwards with his feeding schedule to manage recent irregularities in his blood sugar. *More heel pokes.*

Nicholas and Savannah graduated to Level Two. Nicholas transferred to a hospital closer to his home. Savannah will be in the Special Care Nursery down the hall because she might need eye surgery across the street.

Stacy told me about their upgrade through the privacy screen as I struggled with Torran's disinterest. Maybe she could hear my disappointment. *At least she couldn't see it.*

There are few parents remaining from our start date. Torran is the second oldest child in the Level 3 nursery. We don't know the newer families as well as we knew Nicholas and Savannah, partly because the other parents aren't able to visit for long periods.

I feel sorry for the babies who spend so much time alone

in the hospital. *The NICU isn't a place where one can judge an attendance record.* I'm privileged to know a few of their stories.

There's the father that won't come see his child because he claims he can't handle the medical environment. Another parent comes after work for an hour each day, saving her parental leave for when her daughter comes home.

One mother told me she didn't see any of the lines attached to her son at first, not even the ventilator. Four days later, she arrived and panicked over what she thought were newly applied aggressive medical interventions.

A mother told me that she feels like there is little that she can do for her infant, so she's staying at home until the baby is ready for discharge.

One thing perked me up this evening. Nancy asked if I wanted to try Torran on "low-flow" oxygen for his bath and cuddle. The metered gas traveled through the smallest tubing and nasal prongs I've ever seen. *It was so cute.*

My wee hero stayed awake, looking around without squirming or crying. At first he pulled at the tiny pipes in his nostrils. Then he relaxed as he adjusted to the gentle stream of air blowing up his nose. It must have been more comfortable than the mask strapped to his face and the underlying adhesive padding, because he adapted very quickly.

At bath time, I set Torran in the water and didn't have to worry about holding oxygen up to his face. For all intents and purposes, this was a regular bath for a wriggly boy. He smiled and gurgled, seeming more comfortable tonight than in his previous bathing sessions.

When holding Torran afterwards, Nancy and I continued the "low-flow" oxygen. I dwelt in absolute serenity in the absence of the CPAP noise. My arms held pure joy. Love radiated from me. I stroked his skin-worn cheeks, kissing away the damage. Few alarms triggered. Infinity reigned in each of those minutes, stretching the microcosm of my world beyond any point I'd previously known.

That is what it will be like when he comes home.

It was my only moment of true peace in the day.

CHAPTER 25

MAY 16, 2008

The painted sky on the wall mirrors the clear one outside. *A good sign.* "Okay, Wee Man. Let's try this again." Torran blinks at me and sticks out his tongue as if he understands.

Most days this week, Torran had little success with non-nutritive sucking at the breast. He latched for five minutes at a time, if at all. After his previous forty minute chow-down, I had an immense sense of failure.

Breastfeeding isn't instinctive, so I don't know why I'm being so hard on myself. A full term baby can take four weeks to learn breastfeeding without a mask blowing air up his nose and into belly.

Jen suggested putting Torran on the low-flow oxygen for the attempt last Wednesday. It worked. "Some babies get lazy," she said of preemies chronically dependent on machines. "If we push him for two hours he may get tired, but he's more likely to adapt next time. It helps him remember he has to breathe on his own."

"Could he be intubated again?" I trust her judgement implicitly. I fear the unknown.

"If he becomes septic, it's possible. I think that it's unlikely just for breathing issues. He's progressed very well and the settings aren't maxed out like before. Plus, he might have outgrown his caffeine dosing. We'll figure him out." She advised that some infants use oxygen even when they go home.

That same morning he had multiple dips in his oxygen and heart rate. *Murphy's still with us.* I spent the afternoon forcing fears out of my head and tears from my eyes. Breastfeeding wasn't an option that day.

Torran and I are ensconced behind the semi-private curtain again. I've been waiting all day for him to wake up enough for the Herculean task of eating while breathing. He's finally ready, with the low-flow oxygen wrapped around his head.

Nurse Judith tapes the syringe of milk to the privacy screen and connects the other end to the feeding tube in his nose. She waits for Torran's response to my nipple.

The vibrant child I held to my breast six days earlier returns. He goes to town on the empty food dispenser. Nodding her approval, Judith leaves to feed her other patient.

It seems like my heart beats twice as fast as each second of the first five minutes, waiting for signs of fatigue. Nothing. He's behaving.

As I focus on enjoying this moment of accomplishment, Torran emits a weird sputter. I yank him off my nipple, fearing that he somehow inhaled milk. His colour is yellowy-pink and not blue-grey. The monitor overhead remains quietly indifferent. *False alarm.*

I place his mouth back to my body, but he doesn't latch on. "Wee man, it's only been fifteen minutes. Are you done?" He's not in distress. *What's wrong now?*

Naveen previously instructed me to rub the side his mouth to stimulate the rooting reflex. It doesn't work. Stirring panic encircles my chest.

I consider manually expressing milk and putting a few drops on his lips. It'll be the same quantity as when the nurses use a syringe to place drops on a soother.

A thin stream of milk shoots straight between his eyes when I squeeze my nipple. Torran's eyes flutter open in surprised confusion. I burst out in a mixture of laughter and tears.

I couldn't have aimed that if I tried!

"Oh baby," I giggle as my waterworks mingle with the sprayed milk. "Mummy's sorry." Judith finds me struggling to clean Torran as my conflicting emotions fight for supremacy.

Later that night, as I recount the freakish spray to Bruce, his amusement nurtures my few seeds of hope for a brighter spring.

MAY 23, 2008

Bruce angles himself around the open end of the privacy screen when he arrives from work. Torran, in his red one-piece baby outfit, sleeps against my chest. He doesn't stir when Bruce places butterfly kisses in the gap of his medical gear.

"I'm glad to see you're catching up on cuddles," he greets me. Spring followed him into the room.

Having caught Bruce's cold, I missed a few days at the hospital. I returned yesterday at Torran's handling time. When I put my finger in his hand, he grasped it and smiled.

Instinct? Or was he glad to see me? It brought tears to my eyes. I choked up a second time when Nancy took off his CPAP hat and his tiny mane of straw-blonde hair puffed out. It emphasized his now visible pale blue eyes. *He looked like a different baby.*

He's showing little interest in breast feeding, much like he did before I stayed home. At least there's no sign that he has picked up the cold. I couldn't handle another infection.

As Bruce grabs the hospital chart, an army of tears crest my cheeks. I put my face to my shoulder blotting them. The squatter of unhappiness occupies my head.

"What's wrong?" Bruce hands me his handkerchief. "Is this about the baby from the stairwell?" He's seen the news. The parents of Baby Angelica-Leslie, who abandoned her in January, were recently arrested.

"Did Torran have a bad day?" He searches my face for an answer. This has been one of the few weeks that didn't have any major dramas.

I shake my head. "I want my son to come home."

I'm not forlornly thinking that he never will. I just want him to be at home where he belongs instead of here, surrounded by incessant alarms and sterile touch.

"I know my sweet. I do too," he frowns. "You've been crying a lot lately. Do you think you're going to be OK?"

Last night, Bruce raced upstairs when he heard me sobbing at the computer after I read that a congregation of people I've never met pray for Torran. *Strangers want him to live.* Thinking about the positive love, prayers and support Torran's receiving brought down my Warrior Mother's walls. I lost myself in my sorrow.

I don't know how to answer his question. I get out of bed every day. Then I wait for each minute to pass. *What does being OK mean?*

Torran's getting better, but Bruce and I still face his brain surgery, not to mention the unknown outcomes of keeping Torran alive. Previously, I've said things happen for a reason and that we're not given more than we can handle. *A faker's philosophy.* I don't say that anymore.

What's most true is most simple: stuff happens.

When will it stop happening to us?

MAY 30, 2008

"Of course I peed in the fucking cup!" the young woman with cropped black hair erupts into the phone. She's sitting with one leg straddling the chair's armrest and the other balanced on the corner of the coffee table. Stacy perches on the far side of the three-seat couch, nose buried in a dog-eared magazine.

"I told her I passed the drug test, but she didn't believe me." She shifts her foot as I settle myself next to Stacy, then stretches it into the gap beside me.

The woman radiates irritation. I feel like kicking her foot and her aura out of my personal space. The talk switches to her friend's relationship issues. Swear words dominate the room for the next ten minutes. Stacy and I share our distaste for her deportment with a glance to each other.

"Well, you tell that bastard that your money from welfare is yours. You shouldn't put up with his fucking shit," she lectures her companion a third time. Her volume overcomes the little room, making it impossible to ignore her.

The headstrong counsellor hangs up and, after a pause, continues the consultation with those of us trapped in the room.

"Kim's going to lose everything to that ass." She shifts her position. The slashes in her jeans wink at us. "You heard me tell her he's a deadbeat."

I raise my eyebrows in feigned interest. Stacy doesn't move.

"My kid's here too," the woman says with a lifted chin, validating her presence in the Parent Lounge.

"Oh yeah?" I put food in my mouth, hoping that I don't have to give any more answers.

"But my baby's too big to be here. He's supposed to be down the hall in the other nursery. But because of that, you know, infection, he's stuck in the big NICU." I thoroughly chew on her disdain.

A baby died on Wednesday from necrotizing enterocolitis, the stomach infection we've worried about in Torran so often. Four nearby children showed signs of the illness. Both nurseries closed to visitors and the transfer of babies.

The phone in her purse rings. She dives in with scuffed hands. "Yeah, he's still here," the My-Kid's-Too-Big mom says. She collects her belongings and leaves the room without acknowledgment.

Stacy waits until she hears the click. "I was hoping she'd leave. I heard her mother say she passed a drug test too."

"Whatever drug problem she has, I don't want it shoved in my face when I'm dealing with Torran's issues." Our psychic link becomes verbal.

"I know, right? I'm sorry your baby is too big," Stacy calls out with a bitterness I haven't heard in her before.

Every baby is different, every mother different. Inescapable comparisons rattle our brains.

"At least Torran's having a good enough week. I can handle a little Roughing Up the Listener." I move into the spot previously blocked by a foot. "He's been doing well since they stopped CPAP on Thursday but he still needs oxygen. I'm hoping being off the machine lessens the amount of gas in his belly."

"It won't be long." I know she's not placating me. "Savannah took to the nasal prongs really well." *What was I saying about comparing babies?* She sips from a paper coffee cup. "What about the brain surgery?"

"The neurosurgeon came yesterday. Even though Torran's bearing down a lot and his eyes look like they're being forced downwards, he doesn't think there's pressure on his brain. It's another waiting game." The potential for brain surgery dogs Torran's recent accomplishments. My gaze uselessly scans a posted flyer for the tenth time since we came into the room.

Stacy studies me with the same look I gave her when we met.

"Les, what's going on in there?" She keeps me in her eyes daring me to look within myself.

In this rare moment of privacy, I confess my distress to the woman whose newly cherished friendship I'll soon be without; Savahnnah's going home.

Stress erodes my life. At the hospital, there's no rest; at home, no relief. Bruce and I flag as our hearts struggle through daily incidents, both good and undesirable.

On Monday, during a stretch of early morning starts at work,

Bruce dozed off during his fifth cuddle. Torran slept on the C-shaped pillow I made for breast feeding. Jen and I had a giggle about it before we placed Torran in bed. Later, I blogged the photo. Slivers of joviality like that aren't stemming the tide.

Bruce broke down at work. A co-worker discovered him hiding behind a wall of computers crying.

Our intuitive coping mechanism, where one of us remains calm whilst the other is upset, fails frequently.

"Even though I couldn't be here without him, I find that we're arguing more often than we did before. And it's always about the dumbest things." The staggeringly huge percentage of divorce among NICU parents weighs heavily on my mind.

"I don't know how you guys get through Torran's stuff with the bravery that you show, and I know what losing a child and being in the NICU really means. You're here together and that's so important. He gets involved and you don't leave him behind."

The comfort in her touch coaxes the sad anger away. "Each day is a challenge and it won't improve for a while. You support each other even though it's hard to give more to someone else than you can give to yourself. That's the kind of love that'll get you and your marriage through this hell."

We sit together in silence, two wise new mothers waiting for the next chapter in the lives of our babies to unfold. Sunshine reflects off a window and darts into the tiny room, promising better days ahead.

At least for one of us.

The pessimist won't be quelled.

CHAPTER 26

JUNE 04, 2008

A mournful sound cuts through the NICU's familiar noises. I peek through the incubator next to me. Beside the melancholic woman stands a tower of IV pumps. Her listless face matches the one I've seen every day in my mirror.

We make eye contact. Instead of turning away, I give a silent greeting. She returns the acknowledgement before retreating behind her short bangs.

I come to her side. "It's like watching grass grow, isn't it?" With fewer crises in Torran's days, I've been feeling apprehensive. Susan, our parent buddy, suggested that it's because my adrenaline isn't as high as it was when we first arrived. *I'm waiting for the proverbial other shoe.*

In the meantime, I have to get to know newer parents in the unit if I'm going to have any hope of surviving this confinement. My friends don't call – they know I'm not at home.

"I'm Lesley." The woman's glasses partially hide smeared mascara. She starts to remove her hand from the plastic box, but I wave her still. "No, no. You don't have to let go."

"It's all right. My back is killing me from sitting like this. Darinka," she offers her hand after closing the incubator.

"Your little one came in not too long ago, right?"

"May 25th. Two, actually, at 26 weeks and four days." Delivery dates, gestation and birth weights are mothers' business cards here. "This is Maksim. Marko is over there," she points to an incubator at the end of the row. "He's the sicker one. Intubated. And he has a chest tube. The tall man with him is my husband, Luke."

"Oh wow! That's double heart-ache." Originally, I hoped for

twins. I wanted three children and having two at once seemed the most efficient way to fulfill that desire. This experience with a singleton quashes any notion of creating multiples. The risks are too great. "Why were they early?"

"I was 19 weeks pregnant and Marko's water broke for some unknown reason. The doctors told me I could lose both boys but thank God they stayed."

"You're kidding! My water broke at 19 weeks as well." Darinka stares at me like I'm a long lost twin. "But," I hasten to add, "I only have one. Torran."

Darinka and I trade birth stories, marvelling at the similarities in our pregnancies. More unbelievable than having the rarely diagnosed second trimester oligohydramnios in common, we live within walking distance from each other.

JUNE 07, 2008

Bruce, Jen and I stand beside Torran's bed. Each of us clasps our hands as if in prayer before she pierces Torran's heel to get a sample of blood. Torran's blood sugar dropped after the Nutritionist cut back on his caloric supplement. We're hoping for a normal pre-feeding result.

Although Torran's breathing improves daily, new challenges cut into our patience like stepping on broken glass. A recent eye test showed borderline retinal damage. Torran developed high blood pressure. The tiny BP cuff around his arm is six centimetres long. It's seems twice the size of his first one. Recently, an abdominal ultrasound revealed stones in both kidneys. We're waiting to see if they'll resolve spontaneously.

Looking lover Maksim's incubator, Luke tilts his head at Bruce. "I thought you said you're not religious?"

"I'm not. This," Bruce holds up his hands, "is a gesture. I *do* think that positive energy helps my wee man regardless of what form it takes." Even my spiritually-challenged husband pleads to an enigmatic source of hope for help.

Luke nods. "You can say that again." We formed an easy friendship with the couple, although we see them infrequently. They have a five year old daughter at home.

"At least they kept both boys here," Darinka told me over coffee the day we met. "They were going to send one to Buffalo and the other to London." *That's quite the three way split.*

The glucometer beeps when it finishes. We cheer. Torran's blood sugar is within normal limits.

"Mom, it's your turn." Jen pulls a screen around a chair. Once a day, we replace Torran's tube feeding with breast-feeding. At first, Torran choked a lot and got more milk on his face and my lap than in his mouth. The nipple shield Naveen suggested eased our bungling.

"The shield has a similar texture to the soother he's used to having in his mouth, and the milk doesn't fill his mouth all at once," said the lactation consultant. "With time, he'll learn to manipulate his tongue properly and he might not need the device." *I'm the bionic dairy queen.*

I settle the baby I was once afraid to lift against my side, my hand uncomfortably splayed under the bulge in his head. His forehead and the back of his head most notably show the hydrocephalus.

His swollen brain and the careful positioning by his primary nurses saved him from the typical "toaster head" appearance of a chronic NICU baby. The flattened skull forms because the babies lie facing sideways for so long. Preemies often deveop longer looking faces. Sometimes a shaping helmet is required after discharge to make the skull round out.

Jen stands back after setting up the wires and oxygen. I feel awkward trying to keep the flexible plastic against my nipple whilst holding Torran properly for a successful latch.

Bruce encourages me with a big smile. "At least the shield stops you from spraying his face," he sniggers.

"Go ahead and joke, buddy. I don't have to use it at home if I spray you when you're sleeping."

JUNE 10, 2008

The early morning sun casts meagre shadows in my back garden. Last night's heavy rain pulverized the peonies into the ground. The giant pom poms are like me: pleasant to look at, but broken and bowed because of fluid. Like Torran, they have big heavy heads.

Torran needs brain surgery this week.

That is the most difficult sentence I've ever said.

On Sunday, whilst sleeping on me, Torran stopped breathing. I waited for him to start on his own while the alarms shrieked on my behalf. I was segregated from the rest of the unit by the screen. Nurse Judith was not within ear-shot. With Torran on my chest, I couldn't follow my first instinct and find help.

Then, the echo of Nancy's coaching scolded me like a super-vising grandmother, "Let him have a change to remember how to breathe."

Almost ten seconds later, his heart rate and oxygen level plummeted. He turned blue-grey. I couldn't wait any longer, either for help or for my child to start breathing again. I shook his leg and rubbed his chest.

"Breathe Torran." Earnest words never sounded so gentle. It worked. I felt my heart rate return to normal. My nerves, however, remained jangled.

During other apneic episodes, he wasn't so compliant. Even Nancy needed to intervene. Frequently, he required an increase in oxygen. He needed manual ventilation twice, triggering his brain to make his chest wall expand and contract.

I've been on the verge of panic several times. Torran is 40 weeks gestation today and he's not supposed to stop breathing like this.

Today is Torran's original due date.

Blog Post: June 10, 2008 11:55 p.m.

Happy Delivery Day Torran!

We celebrated with two bite cupcakes and the movie *Kung Fu Panda*. Our gift to him: brain surgery.

Torran will be going to Sick Kids at some point on Wednesday (remember the last time we were waiting for transportation?). Shunt insertion surgery is noon on Thursday. It should take an hour, prep and post-op time notwithstanding.

There will be an incision (drilled hole?) at one of four points in his head (hopefully in the back). The surgeon cuts through the outer layer of his brain called the dura matter, and tunnels the shunt through his brain tissue into the ventricular space that is filled with the excess fluid.

The neurosurgeon says the brain tissue "moves aside" as the tube is inserted. He's a nice man and handled the information very gently, but I'm wondering if he'd describe butter as "moving aside" for a knife?

The other end of the ventriculo-peritoneal (VP) shunt will be passed underneath his skin and through a hole in his abdominal wall beside his belly button. From there, the fluid drains into the abdominal cavity. Torran's body will reabsorb the excess fluid and pee it out. He needs this device in his body for the rest of his life.

I'm sure it's a straightforward procedure for the neurosurgeon (unlike the all day surgery he has to perform on Wednesday). After all, he works in a highly specialized field in a world class hospital.

However, thinking that my baby boy will undergo brain surgery in a room where I cannot protect him or comfort him horrifies me. It's a thought that I don't want, but I cannot escape.

BLUE
JUNE 10 TO JUNE 26, 2008

Blog Post: June 10, 2008 6:52 a.m.

Torran's Three Month NICU Statistics

Today is Torran's due date. Happy birthday Torran!!

-born 3 months early; he is currently 93 days old, corrected age 40 weeks.
-weight 1040 grams at birth (2.5 lbs)
-weight 3915 grams (8.6 lbs we don't know how much of that is fluid in his head!)
-breathed 4 minutes on his own at birth
-intubated 7 times over 8 weeks
-on bipasic CPAP for 4 weeks
-currently on 12 days of low-flow oxygen (50-125 ml/hr) through his nose, breathing on his own and maintaining his own lung pressure
-9 lumbar punctures
-6 attempts for his PICC
-12 head ultrasounds
-9 abdominal ultrasounds
-1 renal ultrasound
-3 heart ultrasounds
-more than 15 X-rays of his chest and belly
-approximately 24 different tubes in his face for feeding and/or suctioning
-at least 12 peripheral intravenous lines
-more than 100 heel pokes for blood
-4 blood transfusions
-daily "swings" of low oxygen and heart rate not requiring nursing intervention, particularly when he's bearing down

-an average of 1-2 "spells" per day requiring nursing intervention
-tolerating 78 mL of breast milk every 3 hrs via a tube in his nose
-just started to tolerate breast milk without supplementation (holding steady blood sugars)
-has the energy to breast feed once a day
-head circumference 40.5 cm (off the growth chart)
-belly circumference 36 cm (his belly is better than last month, although a bigger number)
-five eye exams for ROP, two of which showed damage (resolved for the moment)

Torran has been diagnosed with:
-very low birth weight
-contractures in his elbows and right knee
-respiratory distress syndrome and hypoplastic lungs
-clinical sepsis
-chronic lung disease of prematurity
-grade 3 and 4 intraventricular hemorrhage in his brain
-hydrocephalus on both sides of his brain
-hyperglycemia, high blood sugar (fully resolved)
-hyponatremia
-hyperbilirubenia and jaundice
-hepatic thrombus
-renal calcium build up (kidney stones)
-hydrocele (needs surgical repair?)
-umbilical hernia (needs surgical repair?)

-skin tear (scarred) and perianal skin
abrasion (healed)
-anemia
-biochemical osteopenia
-PDA, ASD and VSD

We anticipate brain surgery in the immediate
future (this week?) to insert a shunt into
Torran's head.

CHAPTER 27

JUNE 12, 2008

When we renovated our main floor bathroom, I chose five dollar blue as a soothing wall colour. It's not working on my overly fatigued nervousness. A stabbing pain grips my stomach like a mauling dog.

Today is Torran's brain surgery.

"Are you almost done?" Bruce's voice startles me through the door. He finished updating his parents in Scotland and wants to depart.

The time for hiding is over.

"Five more minutes."

"Whatever, Toronto," he responds.

It's a phrase bantered about by Bruce's air traffic controller colleagues. They joke it's the pilots' response to them when off the live radio. We've adopted it as our flagship expression for today's episode of taedium vitae - our boring and dull life.

Since we didn't know when Torran would be transferred to Sick Kids yesterday, we left early only to spend an hour in construction-bogged traffic at the foot of the York Street.

Whatever, Toronto.

Upon our arrival, the staff informed us they didn't have a scheduled transfer time because Sick Kids didn't have any beds. Torran's surgery was still set for noon Thursday.

Whatever, Toronto.

Torran fed on fresh booby juice from the "Mum-feteria" for an hour at noon. A bath at three o'clock tuckered him out for the rest of the day. By nine, he managed half an hour of breast feeding. My full term infant remains dependent on the feeding tube in his nose.

Whatever, Toronto.

Torran had three spells whilst breastfeeding today. He sucked merrily and forgot about his heart rate up and breathing. He turned ashen in my arms. Twice, I stimulated his return to normal.

Whatever, Toronto.

During the afternoon, we were told that he would be transferred either in the evening or the following morning. Based on our previous experience, we waited until 9:30 p.m., then opted to go home. By midnight, Torran hadn't moved.

Whatever, Toronto.

Every time someone asked us, "How are you?" we wanted to say, "Lousy. Our baby is having brain surgery tomorrow and he's just reached term age." But we didn't, because most people weren't interested in hearing our depressing news after the casual greeting. Instead, we replied, "Fine," and swallowed the bile in our throats.

Whatever, Toronto.

The day wasn't completely without merit. Torran's received tremendous support, including a handful of visitors wishing him good luck last night. Through phone calls and emails, friends and families bolstered our strength and gave Torran their best wishes. Our hydrocephalus parent buddy tried to get a hold of us three times, knowing what this day brings. It's been an atypically full day of warmth and hope for all of us.

An unusual comment painted a brief oasis. As Bruce and I waited in line at the lobby's coffee shop, I teased him about his stubble. I showed him how itchy it would be for Torran by making him put his inner wrist on his chin. He faked resistance.

"You must be newlyweds," a stranger said. It became our most often repeated joke.

During Torran's surgery and in the days that follow, we'll hold onto these threads of humanity and love fiercely. Torran's cheerleaders will be with us as we sit in a big waiting room amidst other stressed parents, anticipating the summons, "Mr. and Mrs. Donaldson?"

"Bloody hell, how long are they going to make him wait?" Bruce mutters under his breath as he stares out the window onto the Atrium.

Torran's on-call for surgery. He's asleep in an open-air incubator. That we're trapped here waiting for him to leave at any impending moment adds to our edginess.

We missed Dr. Francis once already. Between the staff reports and procedures on Torran, we've been asked to leave the room several times, including during his most recent IV attempt. It was his tenth. I think the NICU nurses are more comfortable finding veins on underweight preemies than the chunky monkey that Torran's become. He weights eight pounds; more than four time his birth weight.

While the intravenous nurse worked on Torran, my friend Sarah brought us lunch. Her unplanned visit granted welcome respite and a better way to pass the time than watching the clock at Torran's bedside.

Bruce and I are alone again. It's past the originally scheduled midday surgery time.

Torran's nurse steps past the curtained family beside us. Her name's Emily, and she's a glowing example of nursing care.

"Mom and Dad," she says quietly (here we have no names), "I just wanted to let you know that things will get pretty sad in here shortly." She doesn't offer an explanation before she leaves.

I understand immediately what that means. It takes Bruce a little longer. He sees me crying, then hears the adjacent alarm. Emily's gentle tones drift through the flimsy curtain beside us.

"The baby's heart rate is staying at fifty-five because her heart is strong and it's meant to work for a long time. But, that rate is too low for a baby in the long run. Her oxygen level is dropping, and, I'm sorry to say, her heart rate will fall too." "Is that what I think it is?" Bruce whispers. I confirm his deduction silently.

My heart grieves for people I don't know forced to endure the death of their baby in a room with strangers. The alarm heralds the end. *Why is it still on?*

I've seen people dying. Family stare at the flux in the numbers instead of looking at their loved one as they grasp onto the wiggling lines as the last signs of life.

This baby's death doesn't need to affect you. I sit between the agonizing event and Torran, a superstitious mojo shield. My imagination succumbs to a vision of his surgeon delivering grisly news followed by my emotional collapse.

"Do you want to leave?" Thank goodness Bruce can think straight. As much as our previous dismissals from the pod frustrated me, I relinquish my blockade. My heart can't witness another infant death.

"Torran, my hero," I kiss his sleeping forehead, "Mummy has to leave. Just for a few minutes, I promise."

"You'll come back to him," Bruce's hushed and pressured words pull me away. "You'll come back to him."

That isn't my child. Torran had surgery at 5:30 this evening, after an hour's delay and preparation in the pre-surgical Play Room. During surgery, a mother from the NICU at Mt. Sinai named Jennifer sat with us in the waiting room. Her son Nathan had a two and a half hour stomach surgery here yesterday. She recognized the blank look on our faces.

"It's a bread and butter procedure," Bruce told her. "They do it all the time." This is his way of coping. I can't move beyond the physical trauma to Torran's head. *But it's better than dying.* Spending the duration of Torran's surgery distracted by

Jennifer's visit saved us from the worrying about Torran's outcome. She spoke at length about Nathan and we were happy to hear her news.

Where Dr. Francis' review of the uneventful surgery lacked Hollywood drama, Torran's current appearance is horror movie worthy.

Torran is unconscious, gorked out on morphine. It crushes my soul seeing a tube shoved down his nose again. During surgery he was pumped full of fluid. He looks like an Alfred Hitchcock shaped parade balloon.

The bloating disguises the shunt tubing underneath his skin. Each leg has an IV line. Both have soft boards attached to them, preventing movement in his ankles. The intravenous tubing lies among the grey monitor cables on his body.

Worst of all, there are soft restraints cuffed around his wrists. His arms splay to the sides. Plastic forceps secure the straps to the foot of the mattress. *So the balloon won't float away.* The nurse refused to remove them, fearing he would pull out his ventilator tube.

The shock of seeing my son, newborn sized but not newly born, in this state turns my blood cold. I'm livid about her decision. I dig my nails into my palm. This *is* my child and I have to fight for him.

"In eight weeks of ventilation, Torran only pulled out his tube once. He's not going to need the restraints."

I keep my hostility under control because there are other parents here. They don't need my anger shoved in their faces.

"I'm sorry, Honey," the nurse says politely with her hands on her hips, "but I just can't trust him. He's a bigger boy now and stronger too. He's not breathing by himself, and I can't risk him pulling out that tube if I'm not in the room."

Torran's prematurity puts him at a higher risk for breathing problems after surgery. The ventilator is a necessary evil. If he loses the technology supporting his recovery, it might have a horrible impact.

But it still doesn't feel right leaving Torran laid out flat by drugs and tied down at the same time. I bite my lip, a plethora of answers screaming from behind my teeth.

And then the dam breaks and I have no other choice than capitulation. *I can't stay here and watch him.*

I leave Bruce to ask his questions and retreat to the window, fearing surrender to the harpy in my head. Storm clouds hover over the city. Lighting highlights a forlorn woman in the window, rain cascading down her face.

Toronto's harbour spreads out below, barely visible in the dark. Lights from the islands form linear streaks in the raindrops in front of me. From fourteen stories up, the city is at peace.

Bruce comes out of the bathroom as rumpled as his boxers.

"I wish we could enjoy being here, this looks like a nice place," he says of the lakefront hotel. One of the mothers we met at Mt. Sinai arranged this accommodation.

"I'd hate to trek back and forth from the suburbs for a surgery," she'd said. "Maybe you can get a reasonable sleep if you're closer to the hospital." Her generosity was more than my heart could bear, and it tapped into a new well of tears.

I don't have to look at Bruce to know how his eyes sink. The shoulders so broad he once thought he could bear anything will be sagging under the strain.

"This will be a great view in the morning," I offer without turning around.

"Whatever, Toronto."

CHAPTER 28

JUNE 14, 2008

My thumb lingers on the END button of the telephone. End
– a small word with a huge impact.

Have I reached my end?

Bruce and I left Torran at the hospital on Friday evening
no less flaccid than he was post-operatively. The day after his
surgery, the NICU nurses continued medicating him with
morphine. He stayed on the ventilator. They restrained him
when we weren't there. Based on the six hour recovery of our
hydrocephalus parent buddy's daughter and the neurosurgery
teaching pamphlet, we expected faster improvement.

The neonatologist monitoring him now used to work at
Mt. Sinai, so she's familiar with our family. Doctor O'Leary
disagreed with me when I questioned the ongoing need for
morphine.

"There's an established pain scale that the nurses follow," she
said. "When they assess him, Torran must be showing some
of those symptoms of pain."

We stood in the hallway, our conversation able to drift into
three separate rooms. *So much for privacy.*

"OK, granted. But, he won't get off the vent if he's pumped
full of morphine." Using the machine decries everything he's
accomplished for his breathing.

Our arguments lobbed back and forth, Bruce standing at
the sideline, a timid umpire, opinionated but unsure when to
make his call.

My determination made a tiny impact. When I called this
morning, Torran's overnight nurse told me she didn't increase
the morphine when he had a fussy period. However, the

ventilator tube remains in his nose. The shred of good news fails to heal the emptiness inside.

My baby boy waits for his champion. But she, *me*, doesn't want to go to him.

For the first time in over three months, it hurts too much to go to the hospital. I'm going back to bed and I don't care when I wake up.

Five hours later, under Bruce's direction, I'm sitting cross-legged on the bed, trying to face the day.

"Remember, you always tell mums they have to get out of bed each day if nothing else." He moves a lock of hair from my shoulder. I shrug my shoulders in defeat. "If you don't want to go today, no one will judge you." *Except myself.*

"Why don't you call and see how he's doing, and then make your decision?" I drag myself to the living room and dial the hospital.

Minutes after making the call, I bound to the genius man who rescued my sanity.

"He's about to be transferred back to Sinai!" Bruce stops sorting laundry captivated by my abrupt change in temperament. "And they're cutting back on his morphine after Francis' assessment this morning." I suspect the neurosurgeon wants to see Torran more alert too.

"So, are you going to the hospital?"

Torran will be with the staff who know him best.

I'm already changing into my clothes. "When can we leave?"

"The Retirement Home" feels warmer than our previous spot in the NICU, the shorter ceiling and closer quarters affording less air circulation. We nicknamed the zone in honour of the three oldest babies who sleep here, Torran, Hope, and Nathan.

Nathan's still having difficulty after his stomach surgery.

He's at Sick Kids, but Sinai keeps a bed for him just in case. Hope is a baby girl born to a delightful mother, one of the most positive women I've met. Hope was born six days after Torran, but her corrected age is two weeks older than him. *It's a mind bend.*

By the time he reached Sinai at noon, Torran was more awake than he'd been since his surgery. The restraints had vanished.

He reaches for the ventilator tube in his nose. Bruce stands up from his stool to stop him.

"Sit down Dad and let him be," Nancy chides. Bruce looks at her with raised eyebrows. "I'm not going to stop him if he pulls it out. If he does, then we'll see how much he remembers." She wants his breathing status back at his pre-surgery baseline as much as we do.

Torran's hand rests on the tube like he's sunbathing and blocking out the sun.

"Oh well, Slugger," she says with a snicker, "maybe you'll get it next time."

Minutes later, Nancy, Bruce and I gang up on the weekend doctor who arrives for Torran's first return assessment. We request the discontinuation of morphine and the vent. Under such ardent persuasion, the doctor agrees to remove the drug. However, he doesn't discontinue the ventilator.

Partially triumphant and with little to do but wait, Bruce and I step away for breast pumping, and to find ourselves some lunch, secure in the knowledge that Nancy has Torran under her thumb.

"I have a confession to make." Nancy's eyes are impish behind her glasses. "When you were gone, I had a little chat with Torran. I told him I was going to have a quick break and he had fifteen minutes to be naughty and pull his tube out."

"Obviously he has selective hearing," I say. Torran's still using the tube as a resting pad for his hand. *Hand over his head asleep, just like Daddy.*

"I think the problems we're seeing with his breathing this afternoon comes from the tube, not his lungs, even though he hit 38%." That was a new low for Torran.

Nancy had suctioned mucous from the tube hourly. Although the drops in his heart rate recovered spontaneously, she manually ventilated him twice to kick-start the oxygen.

The doctor we buttonholed earlier thinks Torran may have a collapsed lung, or that his chronic lung disease is causing new problems. Torran had a heel poke analyzing the mixture of gases in his blood.

"He wants to be off the tube. Torran got himself to low-flow oxygen and this," Nancy points with disdain at the plastic tube in her not-so-tiny charge, "bothers him." Torran's been fighting the tube, frequently gagging on it and bearing down.

A red-haired RT, armed with a needle, steps up to the cot. "The numbers from Torran's blood gases weren't so hot. The doc ordered an arterial sample for comparison." For this blood test, the needle goes into an artery on the underside of Torran's wrist. It's a painful procedure.

"Oh no, you're not doing arterial gasses on my man." Nancy holds up both hands. "Those results don't match how healthy Torran looks or the numbers on his monitor." She suggests that the heel sample created erroneous results because his cold feed caused him to take longer than usual to bleed. "Give him another hour. I'll warm him up and repeat the heel prick. You'll see. Everything will be fine."

The RT starts protesting, then thinks better of it. Nancy sends him away with playful shooing. *She's happy Torran's back too.* There's no better feeling than having a nurse who knows our son so well and is an active advocate for his care.

"Alright Sport, I got you off the morphine. Now, let's see if we can get these feet of yours sorted out. Then," she drops her voice conspiratorially, "we'll get you off the ventilator tonight!"

JUNE 16, 2008

Spending so much time in the NICU is both a blessing and a curse. Torran is my focus, but I'm forced to witness the lives of other families. Yesterday was Father's Day, and I watched a father say good-bye to his baby in a cramped room. He experienced a pain I never want to know.

Bruce didn't want to celebrate father's day; the day belonged to his little boy. Torran came off of the ventilator. He still needs oxygen, but his lungs do all the work.

My wee hero blinks a few times after the camera flash, the blue in his eyes expanding as his pupil shrinks. *He's a real boy with real eyes.*

Nancy lays him down, keeping his head elevated. It promotes drainage in his head. She picks a piece of fluff from the corner of the tape on the intravenous in his scalp.

Torran sucks madly on an orange soother.

"You are a hungry man! I'll have you back on your feeds Sport, and then I can get rid of this IV in your head." The one in his foot failed and his swollen body prevented the attempts at re-insertion in his limbs. His head was the next best choice, even though his brain is swollen.

In Nancy's experience, few preemies diagnosed with hydrocephalus continue to this age. More often they die either from medical complications, or the removal of life support. Though she's handling Torran with judicial caution, she's aggressively advancing his upwards progression.

Torran metamorphosed yet again. After one evening of CPAP on Saturday, Nancy re-established Torran on oxygen that flows through tubing at a low pressure. I easily ignore the clear tape securing the nasal cannula to his face. More noticeable is the large dent on the top of his head.

As the fluid drained, his fontanelle sunk. He's lost two centimetres of head circumference and 190 grams. His head feels like it's floating on my hand. If I didn't know any better, I'd swear he has extreme dehydration, and his head is full of helium.

Dr. Francis told us he didn't expect Torran's head to shrink beyond 39 centimetres even though his skull bones now overlap. Torran has the head size of a one year old when he's technically the age of a newborn.

Torran tries casting his eyes upwards as Bruce kisses his forehead. The sun-downing effect persists but Torran's regained some movement in his eyes.

I caress his lumpy head and assess the crescent moon shaped scar occupying the lower half of the back of his skull. It reminds me of the curve on a computer mouse underneath the user's fingertips. The redness between the dissolvable sutures started fading and the clear discharge is gone. Hair won't grow over that line.

"So, Mom and Dad, does this little man have his own bed to sleep in? Before long, we'll be in Level 2." Without the need for oxygen and monitoring, Torran upgrades to the Special Care Nursery. From there, it's a short haul until - *I love this word* - home.

JUNE 20, 2008

Today, I truly feel like a mother.

Torran's angelic repose isn't hindered by IV or oxygen tubes. Overnight, Nancy got Torran to breathe without oxygen. He didn't have any problems with the change. When he pulled out his feeding tube, I asked Nurse Judith if we could leave it out.

"Let's make him hungry so he takes all his feeds orally." I'm inspired by Nancy's techniques. Judith agreed.

I detach the monitor wires in preparation for his bath. For the first time in 100 days, he looks like a regular baby (with a rather large forehead and funny eyes).

Tucking Torran into a blanket and propping him on my shoulder I head for the door. "I'm just going home to do some laundry."

Judith works with another baby nearby. She snorts a response but keeps watching me until I guiltily return him to his bed. *Would they stop me if I ran away with him?*

Torran's gusty squawk demands a return to his mother's arms. I obediently comply. He quiets his anger to a soft rebuke. Without the pressure on his head, everyone noticed a shift in Torran's behaviour from docile to domineering.

"When he's hungry, he lets everyone know," Nancy said before we left last night. "I couldn't believe it. The girls are in for a shock when they see him next." Jen and Jenn haven't worked with Torran since before his surgery. He'll be going home soon. They won't have long to celebrate his latest triumphs.

The next seven days, Torran must remain on room air and free of spells. If at any point during this week of scrutiny he fails, the clock resets to zero.

We started feeding Torran expressed milk in a bottle as well as breast feeding him. Now Bruce and the nurses can feed him. With any luck, it helps Torran get home earlier. I've been instructing everyone to slow Torran's drinking pace. Sometimes he sucks at the bottle too hard and fast, causing a dip in his heart rate. I don't want him messing up my plan to get him home.

Bruce warned me not to get my hopes up and not count the days before it happens. "He'll be ready when he's ready."

Now that Torran's had his brain surgery, Bruce is dealing with the prolonged hospitalization better than me. He's trying to protect me against disappointment. But I can't help my reckless enthusiasm.

I'm beyond ready for my we man to keep me up all night, poop all day, and dictate our new schedule. I want to complain about the mundane things: that he cries when he's hungry, wet, trying to fart or just needing a cuddle. Most of all, I can't heal my heart until he's with me.

It's time Torran. Come home.

CHAPTER 29

<u>Blog Entry: June 22, 2008 12:38 a.m.</u>

<u>The Hopedown</u>

I can't call it a countdown, because that implies a confirmed end to our NICU journey. Hence, hopedown.

Torran completed two of what will be seven consecutive days of feeding orally and no breathing problems.

All day we regale him with tales of the adventures he'll have out in the real world, the wonderful people who he'll meet and all the love he'll have lavished upon him.

He may not understand what we're saying, but I hope his spirit feels the positivity which motivates us to bring him home this coming weekend.

I love saying that. My son will finally come home.

JUNE 25, 2008

Two rows of one foot square colours in a rainbow pattern hug the room. I stand in the epicenter, my fingertips touching the side of the crib along the wall.

If I let go, this dream might disappear.
In the hall, Bruce practices opening and closing the stroller. "That feels good." A few lithe steps take him to the door. "The wee man deserves to travel in style," he says of the short walk from the hospital to the parkade. We had a car seat installed properly by the police department, and felt like real parents with it the back seat.

When people ask how we're doing, I reply "great" or "awesome" with such zest as I've not employed since the ninth week of pregnancy.

Torran comes home on Friday.

JUNE 26, 2008

Dr. Unger held the enviable privilege of completing our family. Originally, she didn't want to discharge Torran before the weekend.

"I don't like sending families home on Fridays, because if something comes up, a patient's access to services is less reliable. It's my safety net."

I pushed her to reconsider. The holiday weekend holds special meaning for Bruce and I. Since he first visited Canada, it's been our annual tradition to attend our local RibFest. What better way to begin our healing process?

Dr. Unger finally agreed, citing confidence in my nursing expertise as the reason why she felt she could safely bend her rules.

First Torran's home was a plastic box, and then a metallic crib, both in rooms filled with strangers and noise. After 110 tumultuous days, Torran would sleep in a wooden crib surrounded by rainbows in a house where he is the only alarm. Then, I made today's 6:30 a.m. phone call.

No longer driven by eager anticipation, we arrive at noon. Nancy hugs us as we round the Special Care Nursery's nursing station. Pinched eyebrows hover over restless eyes. "Something's up with Torran and it's more than just the spell last night."

We already knew about his overnight apnea. When Jen was on her break, Torran needed physical stimulation to recover from a spell. I could tell she was in shock when I'd called.

"He's just not a kid who has spells, not when he's been doing so well all week." I can imagine Jen rejecting the notion saying, "My Torran?" her blue eyes wide. "At first, I couldn't believe it."

Nancy shared the disbelief. "I thought maybe it was some weird mistake until he did it in front of us at shift change." Torran's third primary Jenn is still on holiday. She won't be discharging him this weekend.

Torran's corner of the alcove is dark. Medical snakes invade his bed. His vital functions display on the monitor overhead. Once again, Torran exists in physical and electronic forms.

"He had a third spell this morning, so I put him on oxygen. We're not sure why this is happening. It could be an infection. His temperature's rising."

I slip my fingertip into Murphy's perfect, cool hand. He's sleeping and doesn't close around it reflexively.

If I let go, he'll disappear.

The morning drags into the afternoon. Before lethargy claimed him, Torran gurgled at his worried parents. His face belied the trouble in his body.

Once again leashed to technology, I hold Torran as Dr. Unger re-assesses him. Half a bottle of breast milk rests on the counter, unwanted. He weakly pushes her hand away. Hiccups, a sign of stress in a preemie, grip his belly. He squeezes his eyes tight. Torran's faint whimper pierces my heart.

Nancy moves supplies around purposelessly on the counter.

Bruce stands behind Dr. Unger shifting from foot to foot, chewing on his thumbnail.

Dr. Unger puts her hand on my shoulder. "I don't think Torran can go home this weekend."

I'm void of words, my mouth a desert. Torran's discomfort escalates. She crouches down and soothes his head when I cannot.

"There, there. Your Momma's here. Momma's here." More tears, the ghosts I thought exorcised, flood my cheeks. Dr. Unger looks me directly in the eyes. Her image swims through the storm I'm battling.

"I think it's worth having the neurosurgeon assess his shunt for infection. If his opinion is otherwise, I'll do further investigations." Her eyes moisten as she stands, waiting for us to take it in.

Nancy smoothes linens she previously folded. Bruce's hand returns to the security of his crossed arms. I rock slowly in the chair trying to soothe the limp, simpering infant in my arms.

Bruce clears his throat. "We knew we weren't going home after the spells started. Do you think it's a shunt infection?" I position Torran high on my chest and kiss his head repeatedly, burying myself like an ostrich in this simple act.

"Given the risks, it's a high probability. Torran's not doing very well right now, and the fever indicates that it's from an infectious process." The shunt is the only part of him they can't check.

An hour later, Dr. Francis strokes the top of Torran's head with hands that two weeks ago saved his brain. He glances back and forth from the monitor to Torran, and then at Bruce and I, his expert fingers always probing Torran's skull.

"Well folks," his gentle tone gives the answer before we hear the words, "I'm sorry to say, this is probably a shunt infection. He'll have to have it out, possibly tonight."

Bruce and I are the worst parents ever. It's 10:30 at night and we're standing on either side of Torran's open-air incubator quietly arguing about whether or not to leave Sick Kids and go home.

Our entire day seems like one debacle after another. It started when Torran's departure to Sick Kids was delayed. I escaped to a bathroom at Mt. Sinai and lost my composure.

Nancy put in a new IV in Torran's head which the other hospital's NICU removed. Once at Sick Kids, he had more blood tests, repeating some already done. *He only has so much blood.* When a technician arrived at 8:30 p.m. to perform an ultrasound of his brain, I refused. The neurosurgeon said he wanted to sample the fluid in Torran's shunt and start antibiotics. The ultrasound would delay antibiotic administration. I made the right call. He's been started on the antibiotic vancomycin.

Bruce is depleted. He's had enough of the stress, the worry... of not knowing what's next. I won't leave Torran's bedside without knowing when he's going to have surgery.

Bruce's sigh is so big I can feel it against my face. "And if you don't get any sleep you're going to be completely ineffective tomorrow when Torran needs you to be at your best." Our previous post-op experience nearly debilitated me.

Torran's nurse enters to work at a nearby desk. I approach her, thankful for the distraction. Otherwise, I'd launch into another diatribe to Bruce about my thought processes. She and I are discussing Torran's plan of care when Bruce calls for me across the room.

"Um, Lesley, is he supposed to be red?" With a look of concern at each other, the nurse and I move hastily to Torran's incubator. The lobster colour covers him from the top of his head to his navel. His legs remain pale and cool.

"Really?" I can't believe it. "Will anything go right today?" Torran's experiencing Red Man Syndrome. It may mean he's developing an allergy to the antibiotic, or that the medication is infusing too quickly. The effect to Torran isn't dangerous, so long as he doesn't display further symptoms of allergic reaction. In another circumstance, this would be funny, Torran replicating his father's red mad cow face. The room spins a little and I have to walk away to sit down. *At this rate, how am I going to cope with another surgery?*

The hospital is so quiet, my ears are ringing. My heart wrestled me down in an empty hallway. *Get off the floor.* I don't want to be on a surface riddled with the cast offs of human traffic, but I can't move.

It's almost 3:00 a.m. Torran just returned, unsuccessfully sedated, from his attempted brain scan. *So many drugs to calm the hungry beast.* The CT was the last of the interventions. They aren't going to try again tonight.

We were frantic about the impending surgery. At 1:00 a.m., a member of the overnight staff told us his surgery would be in the morning. Torran's medical status stabilized and forced the surgeon's hand. He left earlier in the evening to be fresh for the morning. *Why the hell didn't somebody tell us?*

I feel like an ass for arguing with the battered husband who couldn't push himself any further. Bruce was right. Now we're stuck in a crappy room on a ridiculously worn-out sofa bed, too tired to go home; too fearful to leave.

When I'm sitting very still, I have a sound in my ears which is hard to describe. It's a high-pitched soft monotone, neither electronic nor organic. I don't know whether or not anyone else hears something similar in their own head. When I'm not thinking about it, I don't know that it's there. When the world is quiet, I can't ignore it. Perhaps it's my brain seeking auditory keystones to give my world structure. It's been so loud lately.

INDIGO
JUNE 27 TO JULY 19, 2008

CHAPTER 30

JUNE 27, 2008

In front of me, the reflective surfaces and airy colours of The Atrium siphon sunlight from the glass ceiling. Through the invisible walls of the walkways, summer beckons. Submarine yellow elevators travel up and down relentlessly in open-air shafts.

I zip up my sweater, shivering. Torran didn't have surgery first thing this morning. At nine o'clock, a doctor on the team told us Torran's procedure was the third scheduled neurosurgical case for the day, emergencies notwithstanding.

Based on our previous experience, and with physician consent, we drove home for a shower and fresh clothes. 25 minutes after we entered our house, the hospital called. Torran was going to the operating room. Barely clean, we rushed back downtown. The fire alarm went off when we parked underground. Six flights of steps and four sweat-patches later, we had a final audience with his surgeon.

Dr. Francis is a classy guy. He took the time to answer our questions about the procedure and its risks, drawing pictures for Bruce on the back of his notes for a research paper.

An internal delay allowed us to spend ten minutes with Torran before they took him away. He was less frantic with hunger, still sedated by the medications for his early morning scan. Torran looked comfortable, which made it easier to watch him roll through the double doors of the Play Room into the bank of operating suites. I even joked with him to have fun.

My phone rings. Bruce looks up at me expectantly. We're waiting for a call from the recovery room. I shake my head. It's not time to go to our wee hero yet.

"Nancy," I mouth to him. He nods his head and returns to the newspaper he's attempted to read before. Eavesdropping on my conversation, Bruce proves as unsuccessful now as he was the first three times. He hands me his newly laundered handkerchief as I hang up the phone.

"What was that all about?"

"Torran, of course," I sniff. "She called to see how he's doing."

"I heard that part. Then you went silent and now you're crying."

"Nancy said..." *I can still hear her.* I swallow hard. "When she got home yesterday, her sister-in-law called and asked about work. Nancy said she couldn't stop crying for an hour."

Bruce's tears fall on the inside. This baby of ours made an impact, and not just on us. A village wants The Peanut, Murphy, Slugger, our Wee Hero to come home.

This is the third room that's housed Torran in this NICU. We found a nearly wide awake baby in the recovery unit after surgery. Torran responded to us better than the first time he came out of anaesthesia. He opened his eyes and eagerly devoured the concentrated sugar they gave as a substitute for food. When he cried, he couldn't make a sound because there was a ventilator tube back in his nose. *How many times can my heart break?*

We've had a difficult day negotiating the communications and processes of this new hospital. He'll stay in the NICU overnight for monitoring. Tomorrow they'll move him to the neurosurgical floor. Torran is officially a pediatric patient, too big for the NICU.

He has a morphine drip for pain control. I wasn't thrilled about it. However, it also sedated Torran enough for the CT scan of his brain that they couldn't obtain overnight because he was too restless. The receptionist in the NICU mistakenly prevented our entry for two hours whilst Torran had X-Rays.

The morphine I didn't challenge, but I refused to leave his side after the waiting room fiasco.

Torran's still too wiped out to notice that he's full of lines and wires again. *At least he isn't restrained.*

In his tiny lifetime, I've seen tubes and lines invading or attached to nearly every part of his body. None of them bothers me as much as the new one hanging out of Torran's head.

There's a thick bandage taped behind his right ear, a dark yellow and pink stain on its surface. Blue pen ink outlines this seepage from the wound. A random loop of blue plastic suture string sticks out. Emerging from the back edge of the dressing is a flexible yellow tube, the same type as I use to collect urine. A second bandage covers Torran's previous surgical site on the same side of his head.

The opaque catheter inserted in Torran's head attaches to a length of clear tubing with seven valves. In turn, this connects to a complicated looking collection system hanging by a string on a hospital pole.

Gravity drains the tube's contents through the chamber into a low-hanging bag. In the neurology unit, they'll employ laser levels to set it at the right height. The NICU nurses use a tape measure, string, and a squinted eye.

The clear dark yellow fluid in the bag comes from Torran's brain. It's the cerebrospinal fluid that can't get through the blood clot in his head and puts pressure on his brain. *It shouldn't be outside his body.*

The simple system with complicated outcomes erases the happiness I had two days ago. I can't scoop in and pick up my baby when he needs comforting. I may cause an imbalance, draining his brain too much or preventing the flow of fluid.

Torran's going to have the tube for two weeks. I don't know if they'll let me hold him with this *thing* in his head. Once again, I'm a mother to a baby tethered to a bed.

JUNE 28, 2008

The metallic crib with rounded corners looks exactly the same as his big boy bed at Mt. Sinai. In his new digs in the neuro-surgical close observation unit, Torran is the little baby.

An unhappy squalling one at that.

Just before ten last night, the NICU nurse called to let us know Torran pulled the ventilator tube out of his nose. *Nancy would be proud.* The doctors left it out, trialling his response.

During my dawn check-up, she told me he had three spells overnight. The team attributed them to the sedating effects of morphine. Once the doctors decreased the amount of the drug, Torran didn't have any more. However, they continued giving him additional oxygen.

At nine in the morning he kicked out the IV in his foot. In the two hours it took to get him a new one, his activity level increased to the point that the doctors felt he no longer needed the drug for pain control.

He did, however, want food. He tried to eat everything his little paws could reach, including the new IV and the oxygen tubing. We've never seen Torran this agitated. He's not sleeping. No position makes him comfortable. No amount of concen-trated sugar on his soother pacifies him.

Bruce sits in a chair shoved between the crib and the wall. "You'd think our son's biggest problem is his stomach instead of his brain."

My laughter isn't uplifting. "If only we could fix everything with food." We're waiting for his CT scan and blood test results. He might require sedation again, so the doctors keep him on an empty stomach. *I hate seeing him starve.*

One of the two nurses in the four bed room comes to our poorly lit corner. Patients occupy the other three spaces, their ages much older than Torran's.

"Maybe he'll do better if you hold him?" Torran's distemper isn't giving the other patients any rest. I must look shocked. "I'll arrange the lines and adjust the drainage system. It might be a bit tricky, but at this point, what other choice do we have?"

She and Bruce bring the chair and the pole with Torran's bag of brain juice away from the wall. After clamping the entire length of tubing, she places Torran in my arms. Then she re-sets the height of his drainage system with the laser level.

Torran wriggles against me. It feels like he's trying to find a nipple to munch on, but I keep him upright. I'm afraid of adjusting him for both our comfort. The height of his head in relation to the pole directly influences the amount of fluid leaving his brain.

Now that he's big enough to hold, I feel like I'm putting him at harm instead of protecting him with my embrace. In this hard backed chair, I don't have the leverage to rock him. I try anyways.

"Shhh, Wee Man. Mummy's here." I turn my head to the side to avoid breathing on his bandages.

"And Daddy." Bruce sounds hurt. His son suffers and he feels powerless.

"That's right, Daddy too." I make a mental note that next time, Daddy can hold him.

The intensity of Torran's rumbling decreases when he spits out the soother to register another complaint. After half an hour, my hand securing his body weight starts to cramp. Torran is comfortable and relatively quiet.

I'm not going to move - not even when two doctors from Infectious Diseases introduce themselves. We're incapable of making jokes about the Irish descent of one of the doctors.

My alarm bells ring. This type of doctor doesn't just come to say "how do" to all patients with an infection. *Something serious happened.*

Torran's CT scan shows he has inflammation in the linings of his ventricles, the space where the shunt tubing ends in his brain. A bacteria that commonly lives on the surface of the skin is the suspected agent. They want to treat Torran with antibiotics for six weeks.

My head spins as thoughts fire rapidly in my head. *How did we go from two days left in hospital to six weeks?* The longer Torran stays here the higher his risk of picking up a hospital acquired infection. I'll lose my summer with my baby. Everyone we know who was due to deliver this year is at home enjoying their babies.

I was robbed of a full pregnancy. We were robbed of our newborn baby. Torran was robbed of his NICU graduation.

After the doctors left I mutter, "We might not leave here until after the babies we left behind at Sinai go home."

"Your sarcasm is duly noted and appreciated, my sweet." Bruce stretches. "Let's give ourselves a break from this room to let this percolate." The growl in my stomach agrees.

Torran eats before we leave for our supper. He chugs back a portion of pumped breast milk like a university student gone wild. His monitor dips briefly with a particularly intensive suck. From across the room, one of the nurses raises her head in concern. Bruce explains Torran's tendency to eat too fast and forget breathing. Torran recovers without intervention.

Tonight he'll rest in unfamiliar surroundings overseen by two nurses. Before we leave, I kiss his sleeping face, avoiding the side nearing the surgical site. "Even though you're not at home with us Wee Man, you'll be sleeping under the same moon. We'll be thinking of you, and we'll dream of you."

A new moon approaches, and with it the hope of better days.

CHAPTER 31

JULY 03, 2008

Two youthful nurses in cartooned scrubs crowd onto one side of Torran's bed, adjusting the height of the drip container. From a glance, it's impossible to tell which is the student and which the teacher.

I prop Torran in the crook of my arm, poised with a bottle in the other. He's less patient than I, the defrosted milk from April beyond the reach of his opening and closing mouth. *Torran doesn't need sign language to say, "Gimmie food."*

"You have to be careful," the darker haired nurse says as she sets the height of the drip chamber and tightens it against the pole, "because they slip sometimes." She double-checks her settings before she unclamps the tube coming out of his brain. She nods and Torran attempts to devour an entire bottle at once.

Instead of rib festivals and fireworks, our Canada Day weekend involved transferring Torran into the close observation unit of the neurosurgical floor, the insertion of another PICC and more Irish doctors. *Are there any children's doctors left in Ireland?*

I'm starting to dislike hospitals. *And I work in one.*

Brain surgery is the most complicated part of Torran's life, but the team still keeps an eye on his entire body, and the new issues that arose: he's had ultrasound on every solid organ, an eye test, blood tests, neurosurgery assessments, a pediatric assessment, two physiotherapy visits and an upcoming hearing test.

But wait! There's more! We're waiting for a kidney specialist because of his high blood pressure and newly developed critically high potassium. Potassium occurs naturally in the body. It's also used for lethal injections in highly concentrated doses.

High potassium causes irregular heartbeats. Torran received oral, IV and inhaled medications in two repeat treatments to lower the potassium level.

I've given the oral medication before. Sometimes the patients refused to drink it because of the taste. My wee hero gulped it using a bottle nipple on the container. He thought it was food. *Poor duck.* If anyone complains about that drug to me again, I may have to tell them about my son. *What a professional faux pas!*

On July 1st, there was so much happening, Torran barely slept. Each time he drifted off, he woke himself up expecting someone to bother him. Sadly, he was right more often than not.

After a couple of hours of frequent interventions, he became so angry that he screamed inconsolably; it shattered my broken heart. Bruce choked up seeing the peak of Torran's distress. What more does this child need to endure to be a healthy wee man?

A single probe dangles from his foot, monitoring his oxygen. The pediatrics doctor confirmed that Torran's lungs, the only organ we worried about when I was pregnant, are nice and clear.

Torran needs a cardiologist follow-up for the holes in his heart and the PDA. I also requested a general surgeon's assessment of the belly button hernia and the swelling in his scrotum for possible correction. It looks like he has a child's thumb protruding from his navel.

I feel like I've lost what little control I had over Torran's situation. The smallest details fuel my angst.

He's been here for seven days and I have no idea about metrics like his weight, which I used to know religiously. *The only number I know is the size of his head.*

Bruce and I bathed Torran every other day in the NICU once he moved into the crib. Here, we can't. I don't know if there is a protocol for bathing post-surgical babies, which might explains the stray piece of tape on his back for two days. The gunk on his head from surgery was wiped off but the same blood and serum stained dressing remains. Torran's been stripped of regular clothes and now lives in a small hospital gown, open in the back.

I can't move Torran or pick him up without having a nurse clamp and adjust the yellow umbilical cord in his head. Once again, I'm asking another person's permission to hold my baby. If I hold Torran, I remain motionless for fear of affecting the apparatus.

Until last night, I couldn't breastfeed him. The nurses wanted accurate measurements of his intake. He received prescribed amounts of bottled expressed milk. We argued that he's a good eater, but they insisted upon a slow progression towards his regular volume of fluid. *Weeks of emotionally vested steps neglected for a number.*

Last Thursday, Bruce and I were central to Torran's care when we were at the hospital. We held him for hours at a time. Now, we sit and stare, arms empty, neither truly parent nor caregiver, watching grass grow.

JULY 05, 2008

A plastic bag follows an erratic airborne path feet above the curb. Endless cars drive past the front of the Sick Kids Hospital whilst a bronze woman on a circular bench continually breast feeds her baby. I sit beside her with my back to the playing children frozen in the sand. Neither she nor her companion invite me into their perpetual discussion.

"What did you just say?" the incredulous voice on the other end of the phone belongs to Kristen, the NICU graduate mother I met a few weeks ago at one of the parent support nights. She introduced herself to Bruce and me after her presentation, having recognized us from the fundraiser in the park at the end of May.

Kristen gave birth to four premature children, one of whom didn't survive. Since the night she came to wish Torran good luck before his first brain surgery, I've become a moth to her positive glow.

"Torran's been over-drained and now his brain is pulling away from the back of his skull. It could rupture the blood vessels and make him bleed between his skull and his brain." The neurosurgeon said if this happens, Torran may need pressure release holes in his skull. The image gives me goose bumps.

I brush a pile of sand off the bench. The wind blows it between sandaled toes. "His ventricles are too good now," the sarcasm is palpable. *Not good enough to go home.*

His neurosurgeon seemed very concerned about the gap on the outside of Torran's brain. Simple movements like tossing his head when he's crying add to internal shearing stress, and the risk of torn blood vessels. But, he insisted I didn't need to put a warning sign over Torran's bed.

"Does this mean he doesn't need a new shunt?"

"No, just that they can't do anything with his brain the way it is right now. His ventricles are too small to drain. They want to wait and see if the outside of his brain will sort itself out. They've reset the parameters of the external shunt so it's not taking out so much fluid. The surgeon told me a bunch of numbers related to his production of brain fluid but I didn't retain any of them. It could take several days for his ventricles to fill up again for surgery." A blared horn makes me jump.

"But you don't know when that will be," she finishes.

"Our surgeon thinks maybe Wednesday. Torran's brain has to be a little too full of CSF prior to surgery, because some fluid drains out during the procedure." The familiar dampness comes to my face. I wipe it away with the back of my hand.

"Oh honey," she tries to hug me through the phone. "Are you going to get any good news?"

"His potassium is normal," the answer comes out flat. "And the Infectious Diseases doctor says he only needs antibiotics until mid-July." Torran had other positive results, but they aren't curing my dismay.

"How are you guys holding up?"

"Bruce is having a hard time adjusting to the neurosurgery unit. Torran's swung from being a senior citizen to the youngest patient. Bruce keeps saying, 'he should be with babies,' but there aren't enough babies with brain issues to warrant an entire floor."

At one point, Torran's nurse assisted a physician who removed a surgical drain from another patient as Torran started kicked up a fuss, wanting food and cuddles. Without a nurse in the room to work his apparatus, we were powerless to help him. All we could do was lean into the crib, hold his head still and pop a soother into his mouth, which he promptly spat out.

Bruce questioned which need the nurse should attend to first, as a crying baby at risk for bleeding in his head and the removal of a tube both seem a priority.

Under my breath I said, "Welcome to the decision-making of the nursing world." Problems are solved in groups, not one at a time. Torran waited.

"And what about you?" The dancing grocery bag settles in the middle of the road during a lingering pause between cars.

I turn away, staring at the building that houses my life. "I'm not." I'm on that proverbial precipice, hanging on by clichéd nails. "I told a nurse today that all I can do is get out of bed each day, and put one foot in front of the other to bring myself to my son. I can't bear the thought of Torran being alone. It's the only thing that keeps me going."

The weight of unspoken truths slumps my shoulders. I'm not

the same hopeful woman who gave birth eons ago. I wear an empty smile. Herein is my hypocrisy: I'm thankful to so many people for each moment of Torran's days, yet my despondency grows, overpowering the hope they offer.

"Kristen," I pause, unsure whether or not to continue with my revelation. "I can't...What's wrong with me that I keep thinking I need to plan for my baby's funeral when I should be hopeful that he's going to come home?"

Sand clumps together as a fresh round of tears careen into the ground. "I really want to stay positive, but I can't. Torran isn't life-threateningly ill, yet I can't get past the image of him in a casket." I've kept this horrible reality from everyone, including Bruce.

"Les, oh my sweet, sweet friend. There's nothing wrong with you. You've been in Torran's corner since before he was born, and that will never change."

Sitting between the hospitals that gave Torran life and the best chances for his future, I succumb to the grief. The bronze women ignore the sobbing mother beside them.

"I know I don't know you that well," Kristen's words are measured. "You are over-thinking all of Torran's possible outcomes to protect yourself. I don't think you're being morbid. It's harder to hold onto those happy plans because the only time you had them, they were taken from you."

"Please don't tell anyone. I'm supposed to be grateful, which I am, but if I admit to feeling hopeless when he's supposedly coming home soon, I don't think people will understand."

"Maybe, if they knew the full truth, they'll feel too vulnerable. Sometimes people don't want to know our pain. You weren't given a choice of whether or not to hide." The dappled July sunshine fails to warm me.

"You know, when I lost Ethan, I didn't want to be at his funeral, even though people expected it of me. When someone said, 'It will be OK,' I wanted to scream at her, 'What part of losing my baby will *ever* be OK?' But we aren't allowed to do that, are we?" It's like she's here with me, two women consoling each other through the pain; living versions of the statues.

"I know you don't feel strong and life has demanded so much from all three of you. But you can't give in to your sorrow completely. Ask yourself to hold out a little longer and I know Torran will thank you for it."

Kristen's words ease the doubt in my soul. There is an end to this journey that I can't see. My son fought hard to get this far. I can't let my hope implode because his immediate future remains uncertain.

A young girl in a flowery summer dress points past me to the statues of children in the middle of the circular bench as she heads towards the hospital doors, her small hand clutched in that of her briskly walking parent.

Inside, the baby abandoned in a bed waits for one of two people whose touch doesn't cause pain. I stand up, put one foot in front of the other and go to him, hoping I've left the woman lost in mourning behind.

Blog Post: July 10, 2008 11:15 p.m.

Torran's Four Month Statistics: One Month Corrected

-born 3 months early; he is currently 120 days old, one month corrected age
-weight 1040 grams at birth (2.5 lbs)
-current weight 4700 grams (10.4 lbs)
-breathed 4 minutes on his own at birth
-intubated 10 times: 7 over 8 weeks in the NICU and 3 times for neurosurgery
-was on CPAP (mostly biphasic modality) for 5 weeks
-was on low-flow oxygen through his nose for three weeks then breathed on his own without supplemental oxygen (it came very shortly after his first shunt surgery)
-continues to breathe on room air; yesterday he could tolerate being extubated immediately after surgery, although he did need coaching and patience to get through the apnea spells
-9 lumbar punctures
-7 PICC attempts: 6 as a NICU patient; 1 with ultrasound guided assistance as a pediatric patient for the delivery of vancomycin
-15 head ultrasounds
-11 abdominal ultrasounds
-2 renal ultrasounds
-4 heart ultrasounds
-at least 18 X-rays of his chest and belly
-had approximately 24 different tubes in either his nose or mouth for feeding and/or

suctioning, but now he can eat on his own
like a champion
-at least 15 peripheral intravenous lines,
with several IV attempts when he got older
(highest record: 11 times in one day)
-too many heel pokes to count for blood whilst
in the NICU
-6 pokes/attempts for blood tests so far in
July
-4 blood transfusions
-ventriculoperitoneal (VP) shunt insertion
from his brain to his belly
-brain surgery to remove the infected VP
shunt and insert an external drain
-"minor" procedure under sedation to remove
the external drain
-head circumference 40 cm, which is better
than the 42 before his first shunt surgery,
but more than the 39 cm that had been reached
after the first shunt surgery (still larger
than 99th percentile)
-seven eye exams for ROP, two of which showed
damage but have now resolved (follow-up exam
pending)
-three hearing tests, with pass in right ear
and a "referral" (fail) in the left

Torran has been diagnosed with:
-very low birth weight
-contractures in his elbows and right knee
-respiratory distress syndrome and hypoplastic
lungs
-clinical sepsis

-chronic lung disease of prematurity
-grade 3 and 4 intraventricular hemorrhage
in his brain
-hydrocephalus on both sides of his brain
-meningitis post VP shunt insertion (two
weeks of vancomycin for coagulase negative
staph)
-hyperglycemia at birth
-hypoglycemia when the NICU was changing his
supplements (now resolved)
-hyponatremia
-hyperbilirubenia (mostly resolved. Yellow
still isn't his colour)
-hepatic thrombus (resolved with follow-up
in a year)
-renal calcium build up
-high blood pressure (takes amlodipine)
-hydrocele (unchanged)
-umbilical hernia (unchanged)
-skin abrasions and tears
-anemia
-biochemial osteopenia
-PDA and VSD, both closed
-ASD which is still open

Torran awaits brain surgery in the next week,
to next several weeks, for the insertion of
another VP shunt.

CHAPTER 32

JULY 09, 2008

If I close my eyes and ignore the sound of the IV pump, I can pretend I'm a regular mom, sitting on a bench with her normal son during a routine trip to a shopping mall. It's laughable how far that thought is from our reality.

"What's so amusing?" Bruce sits on the bench, hand on my leg.

"It took a fire to get Torran out of the Obs room," I smirk, sunlight flooding my vision. We're sitting at the bank of windows between two wings in the newer part of the hospital. The sounds of the Atrium drift upwards, enveloping us.

"When the nurses said that their med fridge caught fire, I thought that they were taking the Mickey." Bruce looks particularly pale in the bright seating area. Torran, lacking his previous yellow hue but equally pasty, sleeps contentedly on my chest. His bag of brain juice hangs on the pole beside us, filling imperceptibly.

Dr. Francis walks over from the bank of elevators with a quizzical look on his face. I can almost hear him saying, "I didn't grant excursion privileges."

Our brief hiatus is over. He's arrived to review the next step in Torran's plan of care.

JULY 11, 2008

Bruce's mother rocks in the chair slowly, singing to her four month old grandson. His body is the size of a one month old; his head a one year old. She carefully avoids the newest bandages on his head.

Days ago, Bruce's parents Margaret ("Call her Marty," says Bruce) and Peter, arrived to a practically empty house. I was at the hospital with Torran. After picking them up at the airport, Bruce left them to manage on their own. The next morning, we brought them to the close observation unit to meet Torran.

We received permission for all of us to crowd around Torran's bed in the corner of the room. He slept as Mum reached in and tentatively stroked his hand. Dad stood at end of the bed, saying he didn't want to disturb him.

Parents turned medical tour guides, we explained the attachments on Torran's body. After ten minutes, Dad excused himself. Bruce joined him in the sitting area outside the ward.

Mum asked grandmotherly questions about Torran's feeding and toileting habits, and whether or not he was a good sleeper. She avoided talking about his surgeries, antibiotics, and test results. Instead, she praised Torran for being a clever lad who devours lots of milk without spitting it up. She brought normalcy to his life.

When I asked if she wanted to hold Torran, Marty refused. "Oh no, no. I don't want to disturb the medical equipment. He's doing a marvellous job without me mucking about." She tucked a tear-dabbed handkerchief back into her purse. We happily clucked over him for a few minutes more before recovering our husbands.

Yesterday, Dr. Francis removed Torran's external drain in the operating room. Without the need for close observation, they moved Torran to a standard patient room. Since Torran was put in a room by himself, Bruce and I have been sleeping at the hospital, taking turns on the room's thinly padded wall bench and the floor.

When Bruce's parents arrived this afternoon, I put Torran in Mum's arms, moving the IV line out of the way with confidence. *No permission needed.*

Torran gives a fluttering sigh against his grandmother.

"He looks very happy."

"And so he should with that tube taken out." Marty raises her chin assertively.

The bathroom door against my back provides the only anchor in this surreal moment. Mum keeps her head tilted to one side, away from the dressings on Torran's head. Her shoulders don't look as tight as they did during her first visit a few days ago.

Dad perches on the padded bench behind her, recounting their trip to the Royal Ontario Museum. He hasn't held his grandson, claiming he's too clumsy. This second visit to the hospital isn't how I imagined my in-laws would spend time with Torran. At the halfway point of their trip, Grandma and Grandpa have yet to know when he'll be at home.

"What's the latest about this magnificent splodger?" Marty glows as if Torran is the most spectacular baby ever born.

Bruce moves into the room, putting us all within one step of each other. "We're not sure. The fluid is returning to his ventricles but it wasn't enough to put a shunt back in yesterday. The space on the outside of his brain caused by the over drainage isn't getting better, but it's not any worse."

"The surgeon wondered whether or not the hole from the first shunt is making fluid escape from the middle of his brain to the outside," I add. "There's no way to predict when he'll need surgery again. It might be next week. It might be next month."

"If they don't do it next week, then maybe you will be home before we go back to Scotland," Grandma says to the waking bundle. Torran gives her a trademark drooling grin. She eases into the chair.

Bruce props himself on the crib. "There's no way we're going to get away without another surgery in his near future. This hasn't been much of a visit for you guys." Since Bruce and I are sleeping at the hospital, he hasn't visited with his parents.

"Now, Brucie," his mother chides, "don't go on about us. I've told you, we're fine. As for this Splotburger, if Torran has another surgery, then he has two wonderful parents to support him through it."

"And a Grandpa and Grandma who will go do-lally about him from either side of the ocean," says Dad. "Don't worry about getting him home on our account. If Torran has to be here get better, than that's what has to happen."

Bruce shakes his head, for once at a loss for words.

JULY 15, 2008

The door to the hospital room clicks closed. Torran flinches in his sleep. He's in a milk coma and not likely to waken. Bruce is at home. After two nights on the floor, we agreed to take turns sleeping at home and in the hospital. Tonight I'm alone with Murphy.

I draw the thin white hospital blankets tighter around my shoulders. The book *I Knew You Could* by Craig Dorfman lies on the windowsill. Today I read it twice, stumbling with emotion each time.

I'm having trouble seeing the light at the end of our tunnel. We have a perpetual ticket for a constantly derailing trip. Where one problem resolves, another emerges, conspiring to keep us away from home.

Last night, the fluid from Torran's brain leaked out of his head so much that it soaked through his bandages three times. I nearly retched seeing fluid that should be inside his head spilling onto his bedding. The surgeon temporarily fixed the problem with a skin bonding glue.

His "sundowning" eyes worsened since last week. It looks painful. Dr. Francis said, confusingly, the ventricles still aren't big enough to insert a shunt.

Ongoing problems with his brain aren't enough of a challenge for our medical miracle.

We spoke with a hematologist today, our sixth medical specialist. She suspects Torran has a condition where the white blood cells responsible for fighting infection get knocked out every three weeks. It's called cyclic neutropenia. The disorder probably contributed to his first shunt failure. She wants to do further tests to determine if the cause of Torran's problem is inherited or caused by medication.

In the meantime, they're holding his 120 day vaccination in anticipation of surgery. Torran's also confined to his room to reduce exposure to germs. No more "normal" excursions to the lobby or the meagre exterior grounds. *We only had two.*

My life is emotionally and physically restricted to a hospital room once again. Alternating nights at the hospital undermines the coping skills Bruce and I managed in the NICU when we were home with each other every night.

Today is our third wedding anniversary. Neither of us felt like celebrating. Sleeping apart tonight feels like we're on separate continents. We don't question the choice. *And we haven't said the words.*

I am beyond numb. Struck with sheer disbelief, I've lost sight of when my beautiful, strong, heroic and gassy son will come home. It seems as though this is an endless one way ticket. We haven't even started considering the potential for any developmental issues in his future.

Blogpost: July 15, 2008 8:36 a.m.

The Sinkhole

Heading northbound on University Avenue, just south of Queen Street, there is a pot hole wide enough to fit the width of a tire. I can't see its depth as I pass over. I'm not about to stop in the middle of the intersection to measure it.

When I drive over it, it creates this massive "thunk" to the tires as it jolts the car and makes me wince. Many times we've tried to avoid it, but the car still finds it. We know it's there and we try in futility to prepare for the involuntary response.

That was my Monday. I knew that Torran could be denied discharge. I knew his options included staying in hospital and getting another shunt. However, when the message was delivered, a *thunk* emotionally winded me.

The ultrasound on Monday morning showed that Torran's ventricles are expanding in size, once again on the borderline for surgery. His surgeon wants to wait and see what transpires. The fluid pockets on the surface of his brain have decreased in size, which is good news.

Once again, I found myself wondering, "What's the point of all the drama that we're facing? Why is each step of his journey painful and drawn out?" That Torran would need another shunt was always a possibility. Tortuously, we don't know when it will be. If he needs a shunt, I would rather hear, "He needs one tomorrow," instead of, "Let's just wait and see when he needs one - maybe later this week."

Bruce doubts that they would've discharged us because Torran's leaking stitches worsened overnight.

At the moment, he's going under sedation (and intubation) to have more sutures in his head. A neurosurgery team doctor said the area was "macerated" and she wasn't convinced that the new stitches will hold. I'm also concerned about him getting another infection, as he's no longer on the antibiotics and this fluid comes directly out of his brain.

Our lives are in upheaval. Bruce's parents are still here from Scotland, but barely spend any time with us, especially as one of us stays in the hospital overnight. Not much of a holiday. We don't know when we're going to leave here.

A life of upheaval becomes tiring very quickly.

JULY 18, 2008

I clamp the muscles in my leg, trying not to move. The woman performing the pedicure remarks on the calluses on my feet which are thick enough to remove the beard of a bear. With thin lips, I nod politely. *I've had other things on my mind.* Facing another aimless weekend in hospital, I took Marty for a pedicure on one of her last days here. This afternoon, I'll swap places with Bruce and stay with Torran.

My phone rings. I fumble through my purse, hands shaking. I'm not expecting any calls.

It's Bruce. "How would you like Torran to come home tomorrow?"

"What? Are you kidding me?" I sit up so abruptly that I splash the cosmetician. Beside me, Marty puts her magazine in her lap.

Bruce confirms that Dr. Francis plans on discharging Torran in the morning. "Torran's not going to have shunt surgery in the immediate future, so Francis is discharging us."

I can't believe it. My heart races. I can't stop smiling. I want to run downtown and bring Torran home now.

We make plans for the morning's departure while the woman scraping my feet tries to hold my foot still. I wonder if she can do a pedicure on someone walking four feet above the ground?

VIOLET

JULY 20 TO OCTOBER 13, 2008

Blog Post: October 10, 2008 8:13 a.m.

Torran's Seven Month Statistics: Four Months Corrected

-born 3 months early; he is four months old corrected age
-weight 1040 grams at birth (2.5 lbs)
-current weight 7.4 Kg (16.3 lbs)
-his height and weight are 50-75th percentile for his corrected age (length 63 cm depending on who measures him)
-breathed 4 minutes on his own at birth
-intubated 11 times: 7 times in the NICU; 4 times for surgery
-CPAP (biphasic modality) for 5 weeks
-low-flow oxygen for 3 weeks
-tolerated the ventilator tube removal immediately after surgery on his last two surgeries
-coped through his first cold WITHOUT getting pneumonia!
-9 lumbar punctures
-2 PICCs (7 insertion attempts)
-20 head/brain ultrasounds
-3 head/brain CAT scans, most recently Sept 17th
-11 abdominal ultrasounds
-3 kidney ultrasounds, most recently Sept 29th
-4 heart ultrasounds
-over 20 X-rays of his chest and belly, most recently Sept 17th

-approximately 24 different tubes in either his nose or his mouth leading to his stomach for feeding and/or suctioning when in the NICU

-at least 17 peripheral intravenous lines, most recently Sept 17th

-more than 100 heel pokes for blood tests and monitoring his blood sugar whilst in the NICU

-twice weekly heel pokes for investigation of a rare blood disease for two months, then weekly until November

-4 blood transfusions

-at term age (due date) VP shunt surgery then...

-two weeks later: brain surgery to remove the infected shunt and insert an external drain; the external drain "over drained" his head, then...

-two further weeks later: "minor" procedure under sedation to remove the external drain, then...

-three weeks later: a second VP shunt surgery

-head circumference steady at 46 cm (about the size of a 9-12 month old) since Aug 19th

-his eyes "sun set" intermittently throughout the day

-seven eye exams for ROP while an in-patient, two of which showed damage in one eye but have now resolved. Opthamology clinic at the end of this month

-severe hearing loss due to auditory dys-synchrony or neuropathy in both ears, left worse than the right; needs intervention

(hearing aids and/or cochlear implants) and
speech-language therapy
-slow on some milestones: cannot track objects
with his eyes; struggles with turning and
lifting of his head when lying on his belly;
atypical interactions

Milestones reached:
-keeping hands midline and bringing them to
his mouth
-sitting up while supported
-very short memory recall (quiets when he
is about to be fed... although he doesn't
remember that he's ever eaten between feedings
if you go by the amount of squawking he makes)
-baby babble daily
-smiles in response to tactile stimulation
-intentional grasping motor skills
-can lift and turn his head when being held
at 45 degree angle to the ground
-has random mobility of all four limbs
(especially when that diaper comes off!)

NICU diagnoses:
-very low birth weight
-contractures in his elbows and right knee
-respiratory distress syndrome and hypoplastic
lungs
-clinical sepsis
-chronic lung disease of prematurity
-grade 3 and 4 intraventricular hemorrhage
in his brain

Pediatric (post-NICU) diagnoses and ongoing problems

-meningitis post VP shunt insertion (two weeks of vancomycin for coagulase negative staph)

-grade 3 and 4 IVH (may develop cerebral palsy)

-hydrocephalus on both sides of his brain (shunted)

-high blood pressure

-familial cyclical neutropenia

-auditory dys-synchrony in both ears

-unknown visual problem and retinal damage

-ASD between the upper chambers of his heart (may not close for the first two years)

-requires ongoing physiotherapy and occupational therapy to promote his development, and fine and gross motor skills

-the shunt has CSF leaking around the tube through the hole in his skull, making a large bulge on his head.

-scars from heel pokes, the big iatrogenic abrasion and the multiple IVs, PICCs, and surgeries

Noticeably improved or resolved:

-hyperglycemia and hypoglycemia

-hyponatremia

-hyperbilirubenia

-hepatic thrombus

-renal calcium deposits

-hydrocele

-umbilical hernia (resolving!! haven't seen

the hitchhiker's thumb for almost two weeks.
There goes the neat-o party trick: pushing
it in and watching it pop back out)
-anemia
-biochemial osteopenia
-PDA and VSD
-he breast feeds like a champion without a
nipple shield

Timings:
Torran has been alive for 215 days.
Spent 139 days admitted to hospital: 109
in NICU, 27 in Neurosurgery, 3 in general
pediatrics (Halifax).
Attended clinic, doctor or therapy appointment
for 35 days as out-patient (some of these
combine the type of clinic or doctor seen)
Spent 80% of his life in hospital, clinic
or therapy not including the daily physical
therapy exercises provided by us.
Travelled to Nova Scotia on his first holiday,
most of which he spent in the hospital with
a fever.
Not a week has gone by since Torran came home
from the hospital that he hasn't had some sort
of medical intervention or formal therapy.

Seven months after he was born, we're finally
giving him a welcome home party.

CHAPTER 33

<u>Blog Post: October 12, 2008 4:47 a.m.</u>

<u>5 a.m. Party Time</u>

Where minutes ago I worried that Torran went an unheard of eight hours between feedings, I'm now not concerned that he's got an insidious infection developing. After gobbling more than his usual at 3:45 a.m., he is wide awake, giving little babbles and ready to party. When we were at the pediatrician's this week, he said he was happy to see that Torran is thriving at home.

This isn't thriving. This is exerting world dominance.

And I'm not complaining one bit!

However, if 5:00 a.m. becomes Torran's wake-up time, like it was in the NICU, I might have to invest money in a beauty routine to get the bags out from under my eyes.

OCTOBER 12, 2008

In the atypically warm autumn, Mother Nature gives Bruce and I some of the summer days which Life stole. Friends and family fill the garden my in-laws rescued in July. Thanksgiving approaches and we can't think of any better way to show our appreciation for the support we've received. We've opened our home to the people who opened their hearts. It's Torran's welcome home party, seven months late.

The morning we left the hospital, we stopped to say goodbye at the nursing station. Three staff were there to see us off. After one quick picture snapped of our departing family, we left without fanfare. *Just another miracle leaving the hospital.*

"With the two most precious people to me in the car, this is the most nerve-wracking drive I've ever done." Bruce gripped the wheel with sweaty hands. I sat in the back seat monitoring Torran for apnea even though he passed the two hour car seat test in the NICU.

We didn't tell my mother that Torran was coming home. When she arrived in the afternoon for a bon voyage tea with my in-laws, we asked her to check out the bassinette Kristen gave us.

My mother didn't see Torran at first. "Yes," she said slowly walking towards the bed, "it's a bassinette and it's very lovely. What am I...Oh! There's a baby in it!" She hadn't seen Torran for weeks. We spent the afternoon sitting on soft couches, laughing, taking pictures and sharing cuddles with Torran. Life at home started.

If someone told me that I'd be having this party, I don't think I would've believed them. Not knowing Torran's future was the hardest part of being in the hospital. Sometimes it was so painful, that we lived minute to minute instead of day to day.

Stacy and Anton sit under the shade of the crab apple tree, Savannah sleeping in her favoured position in her mother's arms. In the end, she didn't need eye surgery. Her parents seem taller than I recall from our first meeting. Stacy's smile lights up her face. A new set of admirers stand by them, as they share Savannah's story.

We wanted the twins Marko and Maksim to be here too.

Doctors didn't discharge the boys at the same time; Marko had a slower progression than his brother. The night he had his rooming-in trial, he stopped breathing. Luke performed CPR, bringing him out of it. Marko left the hospital requiring oxygen. Darinka and Luke declined our invitation. An afternoon with strangers is both cumbersome and puts the twins at risk for catching a cold. I don't blame her.

Most of the other babies we met went home. One did not. I light a candle for her every week.

"Lesley, my auntie duties stop at poopy diapers," Jessica calls from across the garden. She holds a chubby baby with an orange pacifier in his mouth. *My chubby baby.* Torran eats like a Sumo wrestler who's worried he's underweight.

I sneak my hands around him, supporting his oversized head. "Well, Super Pooper, you're finally ready for some Mummy time?" His eyes, still downcast, are as clear as the sky.

Torran is such an easy baby that we've adapted quickly to our hyper-vigilant parenthood. Scrutinizing him daily for head size, neurological symptoms and signs of attaining or missing milestones is not the life I imagined.

His therapy is almost as frequent as his diaper changes. With the help of experts, we're coaching Torran towards his developmental milestones.

On top of traditional physiotherapy, we started an alternative form called MEDEK. I perform these 45 minute exercises with him twice daily. Torran cries through most of it. Each time he struggles, anxiety knocks my heart.

Between hospital appointments, six weeks of blood tests (they found three blood-clotting disorders), and his therapies, we're trying to live as normal a life as possible.

Bruce and I are rebellious NICU graduates. The infection rate of brain surgery, which comes from the surgery itself, scares us more than going out with him. We wanted to take

Torran to Vancouver in September, but at our first follow-up in early August, Dr. Francis cautioned that it was too early to make the trip.

He was right.

The gap between the bones above Torran's forehead started to swell when he was bearing down. A trip to the emergency department revealed a midline shift in his brain. One side had more fluid than the other. Torran's head grew to 43 centimetres. On August 18th, Dr. Francis probed Torran's head. "It's time." He admitted Torran to hospital for surgery the following day. *My prayers for non-surgical hydrocephalus fell on deaf ears.* The neurosurgeon implanted a programmable shunt impregnated with antibiotics into the other side of Torran's head. His first scar had barely healed.

Torran failed a hearing test administered during that time in hospital. He recently started auditory verbal therapy. In the future, he may need hearing aids or cochlear implants. We might need to learn sign language. *Eventually, we'll know everything there is to know about our son.*

Torran's last admission lasted four days. He received aceta-minophen for pain, not morphine. The anaesthesiologist removed the ventilator tube immediately after surgery. Torran didn't have any breathing problems.

"You're amazing, my precious." I brave the brown cloud from his nappy and kiss Torran's belly above the surgical site. I feel the thin tube of the shunt under my lips.

The single post-operative complication Murphy found was an accumulation of cerebrospinal fluid underneath the surgical site on his head. It's still there.

He looks like he has a sausage under his skin. The second scar is bright pink. Any pressure to the area pushes the CSF back into his brain and the lump becomes flatter. *It's quite a party trick.* The surgeon didn't know how long it will take to resolve. Torran sleeps with his head elevated in the bassinette so it doesn't swell as much. He rooms-in beside me so I can sleep.

The hydrocephalus is most noticeable on Torran's forehead and in the back of his head. The top of his skull looks like the upturned hull of a boat. My brain superimposes the old man from the NICU on his edible infant face. The fluffs of hair at the top and sides of his head make him look like the character Sloth from *Goonies*.

Bruce and I are making good on our Ides of March promises to Torran: he's been to the Canadian National Exhibition and on a trip to Halifax.

With Dr. Francis' consent, we went to the CNE in August. A performer who looked like a drunk, crazy professor came up to the stroller, peered in at Torran and started to take it away.

I grabbed the handle. "Do not take my child." The man kept going. "Do *not* take my child," I growled. "I'm not joking." A moment of incredulousness flashed across his face. "He just came out of the hospital." The man's lucky he let go at that point or I would've created a scene.

In September, we travelled to Halifax. We choose the area because it has a hospital capable of children's brain surgery, as much as for its tourism. Murphy spiked a fever and we spent our first family trip in IWK hospital.

The possibility of shunt infection persists in varying degrees for a year after surgery. "In the first three months post-op, any fever is a shunt infection unless proven otherwise," we were told. Two days and a series of hospital investigations after Torran's fever started, he developed a runny nose. A silly cold virus ruined our trip.

Reminders of Torran's unique start in life punctuate our normalcy. Scars are all over his body in different shapes and sizes. Hanging from a shelf in Torran's room is a string of 30 Bravery Beads. Each bead represents a procedure or event he experienced at Sick Kids in his last month, save for one: the going home bead.

One day, he'll know the full extent of his story. For now, Torran's happier attempting to get his poop everywhere with limbs that won't stop wriggling.

Surrounded by rainbows, I do the "mom rock" at Torran's bedroom window. Below, the pillars of our strength enjoy easy companionship. Bruce stands at the barbeque with a beer in his hand. He sees me at the window and tilts his head with concern. I shake my head and wave. Torran sleeps against my shoulder. *No drama today.*

Torran has a laundry list of problems and a longer list of joys. He's a baby who gurgles and smiles to our delight. He eats with gusto. Best of all, he loves being held despite all the painful touch he experienced during the first 136 days of his life.

Our experiences traumatized our family and we'll never forget the pain. It's hard for some people to understand that, although we feel defrauded, we'd choose the same agonizing path again. But, we'd never wish it on our worst enemy. Others assume that everything is okay now that Torran's home. We simply respond that he's a complicated wee man, and his future is yet unwritten.

We must be patient. Torran will tell us what he needs and the life he wants to lead.

Whatever comes, he embodies our love. We are honoured by his fight to come home.

Blog Post: October 13, 2008 8:58 p.m.

If Only Every Day Were Like Sunday

At our BBQ yesterday, I paused before walking inside the house. Behind me the din of people chatting, children playing, and birds singing saluted the last warm days of autumn. Spontaneously and surprisingly, these words erupted from my mouth:

I love my baby
I love my family
I love my friends
I love my life

Dear Preemie Parent,

Be connected. Your heartache is profound. Know that you are not alone in your sorrow. Whatever your feelings, be they anger, resentment, guilt, joy or sadness, they are completely normal. Seek out other parents and families of the preemie community. You'll find understanding and welcome in ways that you'd never expect.
Be kind to yourself. Don't burden your bruised heart with guilt. You may never know what caused your child's prematurity. Without any indication as to how or why, a normal skin bacterium colonized the lining of my uterus. I had no foreknowledge or symptoms. It makes my uterus "hostile" to pregnancy. I was lucky to bring Torran home.
Be patient with yourself. The trauma you're experiencing may never go away. Torran is six and I still see the boy in the box when I look at him. There were days when I didn't think we'd make it this far. There are days when I don't know how far ahead he'll travel. Sometimes, the only way I cope through the day is getting out of bed and putting one foot in front of the other.
Be hopeful. Your love for your child will never end, no matter when she or he comes home, or for how long she or he will be present on this earth. Your children are on a path that no parent expects. Each destination, like each baby, is unique and meaningful. Hold on to a precious minute to get through a difficult day. Take the pain of a difficult day and use it as motivation towards a purposeful life.
Every life is of value. Cherish each moment of your miracle.
I wish you peace and every measure of success,

Lesley